SING OUR SONGS LET'S SING OUR SONGS LET'S SING OUR SONGS

D1094102

A SINGING SCHOOL

OUR SONGS

•••••••••••••••••••••••••••• NEW EDITION

Editors:

Theresa Armitage
Peter W. Dykema
Gladys Pitcher

Advisory Editors:

Charles H. Farnsworth
Herman F. Smith

Art Editor:

Martha Powell Setchell

BOSTON · C · C · BIRCHARD and COMPANY

We wish to thank The Macmillan Company, publishers, for permission to use the poem, "The Little Turtle" by Vachel Lindsay, from *Collected Poems,* in the song on Page 140; the Scott Foresman Company, owners of the copyright, for permission to use the song, "The Daily Express" (The Train) by Charles Harvey on Page 68; Miss Fanny A. Buchanan for permission to use her poem, "Good Morning," in the song on Page 6; Miss Alys Bentley for permission to use her songs, "Big Brown Bear" on Page 57, "My Fiddle" on Page 116, "Who Has Seen the Wind?" on Page 63, and "A Wish" on Page 34; and Miss Cleva Carson for permission to use the song, "The Woodpecker," written by one of her classes, on Page 117.

We also wish to thank all those who have written words and music for OUR SONGS. You will find their names in the Index beginning on Page 173.

We especially want to thank Margery Armitage for the poems, and J. Lilian Vandevere and David Stevens for the poems and music they have written for us.

The Books of

A SINGING SCHOOL

I OUR FIRST MUSIC—Complete in itself; for the teacher

II OUR SONGS
III MERRY MUSIC
IV WE SING
V OUR LAND OF SONG
VI MUSIC EVERYWHERE

Each complete in three units:
a. Student's Edition
b. Book of Accompaniments
c. Teacher's Manual

VII SING OUT!
VIII LET MUSIC RING!

I–IV HAPPY SINGING *
I–VIII MUSIC IN THE AIR *

Each complete in two units:
a. Student's Edition
b. Teacher's Book—manual and accompaniments

* For combined classes

RCA Victor Records are available for use with this book.

5-55

Dear Boys and Girls:

This is your book of songs. We know that you will use it often and that you will enjoy singing the songs.

You will find many songs which have come from our own land and from many other lands. Other songs have been written just for you.

Esther Boston Bristol, Adelaide True and Charlotte Washburn have drawn the lovely pictures for you.

We hope this book will bring you many happy hours.

The Editors and Publishers

WASTE
T
W
B

MUSIC

AT HOME

MY MORNING SONG

The first thing in the morn-ing When I get out of
bed, I sing and sing a hap-py song That
comes in-to my head. I don't know where it
comes from, It just be-gins, you see, And
ritard
in time
then I sing and sing and sing, As hap-py as can be.

GOOD MORNING

ALL OF US
Good morn-ing, sky, Good morn-ing, sun,
Good morn-ing, lit-tle winds that run!
Good morn-ing, birds, Good morn-ing, trees,
And creep-ing grass, and brown-ie bees.
ONE VOICE
3
How did you find out it was day?

ritard
Who told you night had gone a - way?
ALL OF US
in time
I'm wide a - wake, I'm up now, too,
I'll be right out and play with you!

WHEN MOTHER SEWS

When my moth - er sits and sews,
In and out her nee - dle goes;
Moth - er sews such love - ly things,
And while she sews she hums and sings
Hm

Hm

COPYING MOTHER

1. Moth - er irons the clothes so,
2. Moth - er sweeps the floor so,
So, so, so, so.
So, so, so, so.
Moth - er irons the clothes so,
Moth - er sweeps the floor so,
So, so, so.
So, so, so.

What other things that mother does can we sing about, or act out?

I WALK AND TALK WITH FATHER

Some days I like to take a walk,
I like to hear him laugh and talk,
And so I go with fa - ther.
It's fun to be with fa - ther.
We come to fenc-es we have to climb,
And I'm nev - er far be-hind fa - ther;
We have a ver - y pleas-ant time,

When I go out with fa - ther.

MY HUMMING TOP

1. Oh, my hum - ming top is yel - low;
2. Oh, my top is ver - y bus - y,
Now I'll wind him with a spring.
Now he's spin - ning round and round,
If you watch the lit - tle fel - low,
But he some - times gets so diz - zy
Pret - ty soon you'll hear him sing.
That he tum - bles to the ground.

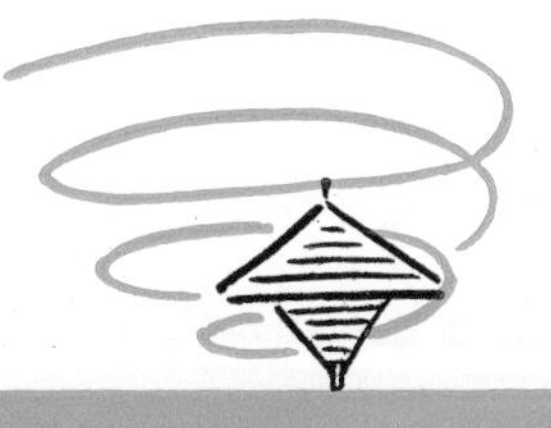

COOKIES

1. My moth-er's mak-ing cook-ies now, she
2. My dad-dy likes the lit-tle stars, he

makes them now and then, And some are stars and
says they're like my eyes. I like to think my

some are hearts and some are lit-tle men.
eyes are bright like stars up in the skies.

The cook-ie men are ver-y good, she
But I like cook-ie stars, I guess, be-

al-ways makes a few. I hope it does not
cause they're nice and sweet. If you'll just come on

PUSSY

hurt them when I bite them right in two.
cook - ie day we'll have a cook - ie treat.

HOT GINGERBREAD

1. Moth-er's bak-ing gin-ger-bread, Bak - ing some for
2. Moth-er's nice hot gin-ger-bread, "Come and eat it

me, she said. Nice and brown, best in town,
now," she said. "Not too fast, make it last"

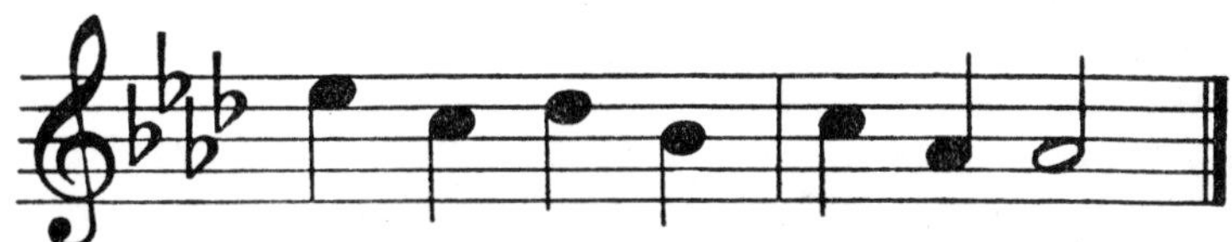

Moth-er's bak - ing gin-ger-bread.
Moth-er's nice hot gin-ger-bread.

This tune may be sung whenever it fits in with the music.

Yum, yum, gin-ger-bread!

STRANGE!

1. A bub - ble is a fun - ny thing,
2. A bub - ble is a fun - ny thing,
It's ver - y small at first,
It's most - ly made of air.
But when you blow to make it grow,
You start to blow, and next you know,
It's ver - y sure to burst.
It simp - ly is - n't there.

B

OCCUPATIONS

1. This is how I play All the live-long day;
2. When I'm not so small, When I'm big and tall,
First I play that I'm a sail-or,
I shall real-ly be a fli-er,
Then pre-tend I drive a trail-er,
Sail-ing high, and HIGH and HIGH-ER!
I play post-man, too; That is what I do!
That is what I'll be, Just you wait and see!
SOAP

RAGTAG AND BOBTAIL

1. Rag - tag and Bob - tail,
2. Rag - tag and Bob - tail,
A span - iel and a Bos - ton ter - ri - er,
It's hard to tell which one's the mer - ri - er,
Rag - tag and Bob - tail,
Rag - tag and Bob - tail,
They both are reg - u - lar dogs.
They both are reg - u - lar dogs.

WHAT I LIKE

The milk-man's horse is sleek and fat,
In sum-mer time he wears a hat,
A hat that lets his ears come through,
I like a hat like that, don't you?
I like to have my ears come thro' like that, don't you?
MILK

MY FUNNY JUMPING JACK

1. O see the fun - ny Jump - ing Jack,
2. I pull the string and then the elf
3. And when it's time to go to bed
He has two fronts but has no back,
Will jump so hard he kicks him - self,
He dan - gles limp - ly by the head,
Both sides are just the same,
This fel - low kicks him - self—
But nev - er shuts his eyes,
Both sides are just the same.
This fel - low kicks him - self.
No, nev - er shuts his eyes.

HOBBY HORSE

Hi, po-ny, ho, now, Hi, po-ny, ho, now,
Trot and run, get a - long, lit-tle hob-by-horse,
Out in the field on a sum-mer day,
Oh, what fun when I
ride on my hob-by horse,
O-ver the fields a - way.

TROT, TROT, TROT

Trot, trot, trot, trot, trot, trot, trot, trot, trot lit-tle po-ny,
trot. Lift your lit-tle feet so high, Toss your head as
you pass by. Trot, trot, trot, trot, trot, trot, trot, trot,
trot, lit-tle po-ny, trot! Trot, trot, trot, trot,
trot, trot, trot, trot, trot, lit-tle po-ny, stop! Whoa!

HE WHISTLED JUST THE SAME

1. When Bob-by cut his hand one day, the
2. His sis-ter said "I'm sure it hurts, it
bus-y doc-tor came; It hurt a lot, but
real-ly seems a shame!" But Bob-by said, "It's
Bob-by smiled, and whis-tled just the same.
all right, Sis," and whis-tled just the same.
(Whistle) It hurt a lot, but
But Bob-by said "It's
Bob-by smiled, and whis-tled just the same.
all right, Sis," and whis-tled just the same.

After the last verse let's whistle the last eight measures.

MUSIC ON THE AIR

1. I sit be - side the ra - di - o,
2. Some - times they have a sto - ry hour,
I like to hear it play,
And sing a - bout Bo Peep,
But Dad - dy turns a knob or two
But once I missed the best of it
And then it goes a - way.
Be - cause I fell a - sleep.

AMERICA

My coun-try, 'tis of thee, Sweet land of lib - er-ty,
Our fa-thers' God, to Thee, Au - thor of lib - er-ty,
Of thee I sing. Land where my fa - thers died!
To Thee we sing. Long may our land be bright
Land of the Pil - grim's pride! From ev - 'ry
With free-dom's ho - ly light; Pro - tect us
moun - tain side, Let free - dom ring!
by Thy might, Great God, our King!

NELLY BLY

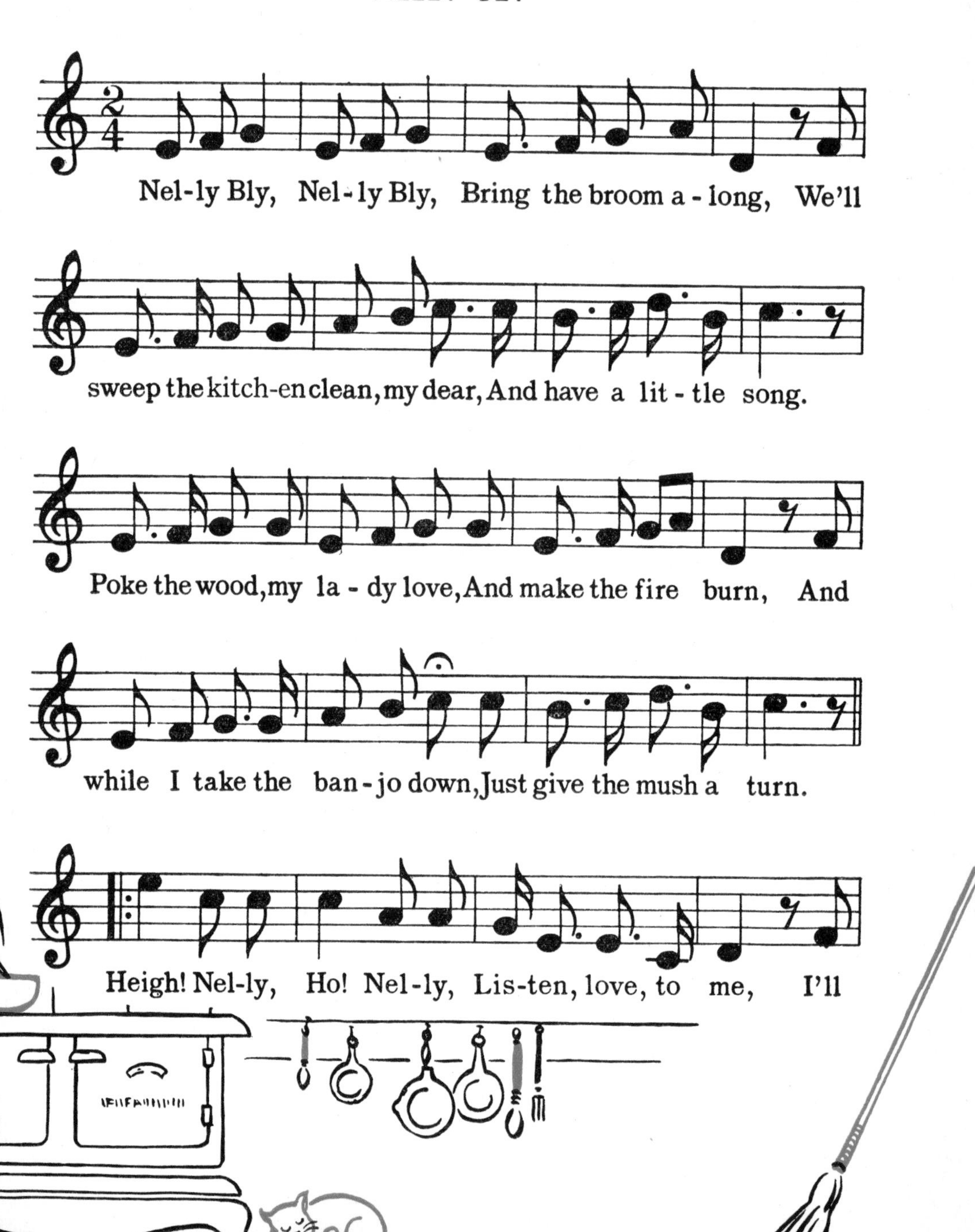
Nel-ly Bly, Nel-ly Bly, Bring the broom a-long, We'll
sweep the kitch-en clean, my dear, And have a lit-tle song.
Poke the wood, my la-dy love, And make the fire burn, And
while I take the ban-jo down, Just give the mush a turn.
Heigh! Nel-ly, Ho! Nel-ly, Lis-ten, love, to me, I'll

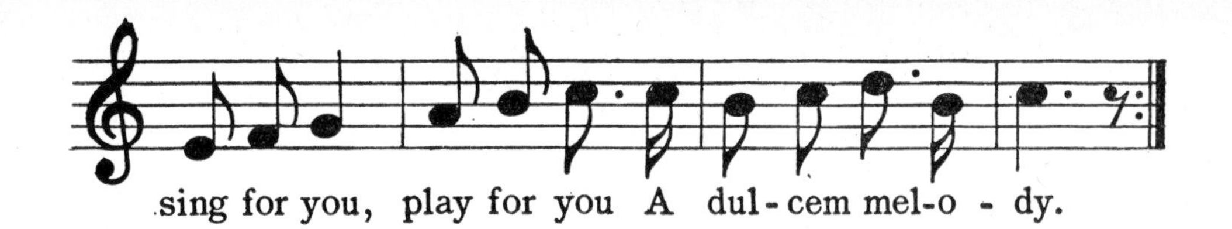
sing for you, play for you A dul - cem mel-o - dy.

SILENT NIGHT

1. Si - lent night! Ho - ly night! All is calm,
2. Si - lent night! Ho - ly night! Shep-herds quake
all is bright Round yon vir - gin moth - er and Child!
at the sight! Glo - ries stream from heav - en a - far,
Ho - ly In - fant, so ten - der and mild, Sleep in
Heav'n-ly hosts sing, "Al - le - lu - ia, Christ the
heav - en - ly peace, Sleep in heav-en-ly peace.
Sa-viour is born! Christ the Sa-viour is born!"

BILLY MAGEE MAGAW
1. There were three crows sat on a tree,
2. Said one old crow un - to his mate,
3. Said one old crow, "I heard them say,"
4. So to the field they took their flight,
Bil-ly Ma-gee, Ma - gaw. There were three crows sat
Bil-ly Ma-gee, Ma - gaw. Said one old crow un-
Bil-ly Ma-gee, Ma - gaw. Said one old crow, "I
Bil-ly Ma-gee, Ma - gaw. So to the field they
on a tree, Bil-ly Ma-gee, Ma - gaw. There
to his mate, Bil-ly Ma-gee, Ma - gaw. Said
heard them say," Bil-ly Ma-gee, Ma - gaw. Said
took their flight, Bil-ly Ma-gee, Ma - gaw. So
CORN
BEAN

were three crows sat on a tree, And
one old crow un - to his mate, "What
one old crow "I heard them say The
to the field they took their flight And
they were black as crows could be,
shall we do for food to eat?"
far - mer planted his corn to - day,"
raised the farm - er's corn that night,
And they all flapped their wings and cried,
"Caw! Caw! Caw! Caw!" Bil-ly Ma-gee, Ma- gaw!
MORE CORN

SUCH A DIFFERENCE

1. When Moth - er says, "It's time for bed,
The clock is strik - ing eight!"
It's ver - y hard to say "Good-night,"
I'd so much rath - er wait.
2. When Moth - er says, "Get up, my dear,
The sun's be - gun to peep!"
It's ver - y hard to say "I will!"
I'd so much rath - er sleep.
3. But then I guess it's rath - er nice
To go to bed at eight,
For sleep will make me good and strong
So I can swim and skate.
4. And if I don't get up on time
As soon as day's be - gun,
I'm ver - y much a - fraid that I
Shall miss a lot of fun.

CRADLE SONG

Quietly
1. Ho - ro, ba - by, loo, loo, loo,
2. Ho - ro, ba - by, lull - a - by,
3. Fa - ther's gone to count the sheep,
Sleep and dream, my lamb - kin.
Sleep and dream, my lamb - kin.
Sleep and dream, my lamb - kin.
Dream - land fair - ies wait for you,
Sis - ter's com - ing by and by,
Soon they too will be a - sleep,
Sleep and dream.
Sleep and dream.
Sleep and dream.

Swedish mothers sing this song to their children.

GUESS WHO I AM

1. I pass each joy - ful sum - mer day
2. I'm al - ways bus - y, nev - er play
A - mong my friends, the flow'rs,
As oth - er crea - tures do;
And ev - 'ry night I bear a - way
If you should pic - nic some fine day,
Their gifts for win - ter hours.
I'm sure to be there, too.

LITTLE BUNNY HOPS

Lit-tle bun-ny hops, hunt-ing clo-ver tops,
Hun-gry for his break-fast in the morn - ing.
Nib-bling, nib-bling, nib-bling, nib-bling,
softer
Nib-bling, nib-bling, nib-bling, nib-bling,
Hap-py with his break-fast in the morn - ing.

COME, LITTLE CHIPMUNK

1. Come, come, gay lit-tle chip-munk, No one here will
2. Come, come, gay lit-tle chip-munk, May-be we can
harm you; Come, come, gay lit-tle chip-munk,
charm you; Come, come, gay lit-tle chip-munk,
Come and nev-er fear. We love to see you
Near but not too near. The best of pea-nuts
scam-per by, With bush-y tail and bead-y eye,
you shall try, We al-ways have a good sup-ply,
So come right up and don't be shy, We're all friends here.
So come right up and don't be shy, We're all friends here.

BUTTERFLIES

1. But-ter-flies here, but-ter-flies there,
2. But-ter-flies brown, but-ter-flies white,
But-ter-flies flit-ting in the sun-lit air.
But-ter-flies float-ing where the flow'rs are bright.
LITTLE BROWN BUG
1. Lit-tle brown bug, you run when I pass,
2. Lit-tle brown bug, I'm lit-tle like you.
You are a-fraid and hide in the grass.
May-be I seem a gi-ant to you.

A WISH

I wish that I could float through the air,
And cir - cle round and a - round;
I wave my arms and hop and skip,
But can - not leave the ground.
Do not go, but-ter-fly, but-ter-fly, but-ter-fly.

HELLO!

f SOME OF US OTHERS STILL OTHERS
mf
p
Hel - lo! Hel - lo! Hel - lo!
1st GROUP 2nd GROUP 3rd GROUP
Hel - lo! Hel - lo! Hel - lo!
ALL
The ech - oes hear each note I sing,
They're al - ways out of sight you know,
And send it back to me.
I guess they hide from me.
SOME OF US OTHERS STILL OTHERS
Hel - lo! Hel - lo! Hel - lo!

GEESE
Children 1. Hear those geese as they wad-dle down the lane,
2. Hear them hiss as they wad-dle in a row;
Geese S-ss S-ss
Hiss-ing like the steam from a rail-road train.
Why are geese so cross when I say "hel - lo"?
S-ss S-ss
A NOISY BIRD
Hear the rap - tap - tap on the bark of the tree,
I know who's tap-ping, You can't fool me.

MOVING DAY

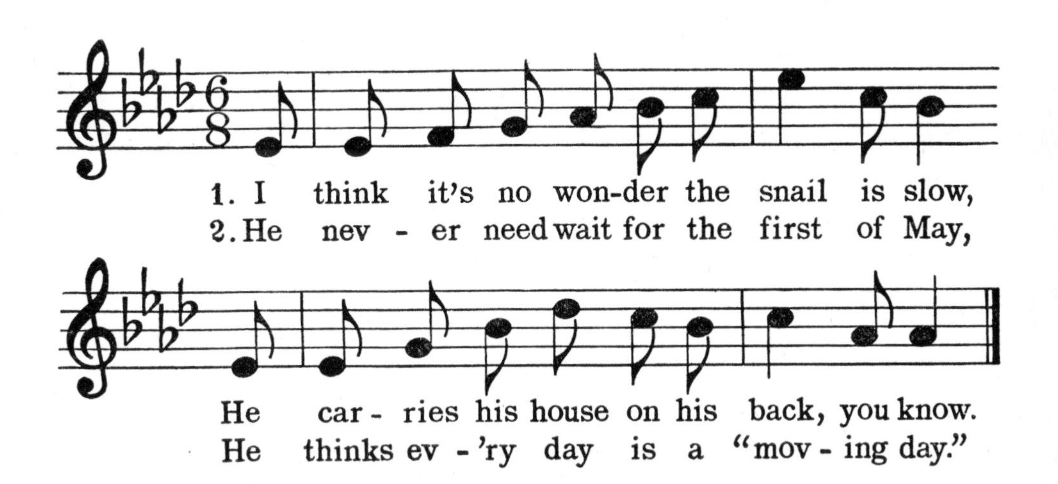
1. I think it's no won-der the snail is slow,
2. He nev - er need wait for the first of May,
He car - ries his house on his back, you know.
He thinks ev - 'ry day is a "mov - ing day."

FUNNY BUNNY

Lit-tle rab-bit, tell us, why you are so fun - ny,
Why you jump and thump so, Fun-ny lit - tle bun-ny!
Why you jump so, why you thump so, Fun-ny lit-tle bun-ny!

THE LAMBKIN

1. Ba - by lamb - kin, go to rest, Safe in your
2. Ba - by lamb, the pines have grown Black as a
coz - y fold; Run to moth-er's wool-ly breast,
twi - light crow; Stay no long-er here a - lone,
Run from the dark and cold. The thrush is
Go, lit - tle lamb - kin, go! The mist - y
sing-ing his last good night, The cot - tage
shad-ows are creep - ing round, The night wind's
win - dow is red with light, The owl is a -
voice has a lone - some sound; Your moth - er is
HOME

wake, for his day's be-gun. Run, lit-tle lamb-kin, run.
call-ing her lit - tle one. Run, lit-tle lamb-kin, run.
ALL IN THE TREE
1. "What a pleas-ant place to be,
2. Then a boy said, "Look at me,
And the rent is al-ways free,"
I can go as high as he,
Said the fluf - fy lit-tle bird
I am climb-ing to the top
In the tall green tree.
Of the tall green tree."

HOP, LITTLE FROG

1. Hop, hop, hop, lit - tle frog.
2. Swim, swim, swim, lit - tle frog.
Moth-er is wait - ing by the old gray log;
Moth-er is watch-ing by the old gray log;
Hop, hop, hop, lit - tle frog.
Swim, swim, swim, lit - tle frog.
Moth-er is wait - ing, So hop, lit-tle frog!
Moth-er is watch-ing, So swim, lit-tle frog!

What other things can the frog do? Can he sing?

ORANGE MOON

1. See the pret - ty o - range moon,
2. If it had a string, you see,
Like a lit - tle toy bal - loon;
I could pull it down to me;
Some - one took it out to play,
Then I'd hold it good and tight
Then it flew a - way.
Through the whole long night.
Let some of us hum this tune, while others sing the song.
Hum
MAIN ST.

SHOPPING

When Mother will take me,
A-shopping I go,
And often I meet
Sev'ral people I know.

The traffic policeman,
The postman in gray,
A funny black Scottie
I see every day.

WHEN THE POSTMAN COMES
1. Ev - 'ry day at nine o' - clock,
2. Now let's see what he has brought,
3. Some - day I shall grow up, too,
Aft - er - noons at four;
One and two and three;
We will wait and see;
When I hear the post - man knock, I
Sis - ter al - ways has a lot, But
I shall write to *you* and *you*, And
run and o - pen the door.
not a let - ter for me.
you'll be writ - ing to me.
U-S-MAIL

THE POLICEMAN

Some of Us
Who al - ways helps his fel - low - men?
Others
The po - lice - man! The po - lice - man!
1st Group
Who brings lost chil - dren home a - gain?
STOP
SAFETY
SCHOOL
CROSSING
ZONE

2nd GROUP
The po - lice - man! The po - lice - man!
1st GROUP
Who an - swers ques - tions ev - 'ry day
To help the peo - ple find their way?
When we're in trou - ble, we all say,
ALL TOGETHER
Oh, po - lice - man! Oh, po - lice - man!

THE COBBLER

Girls 1. A - rap - tap - tap, a - rap - tap - tap,
2. A - rap - tap - tap, a - rap - tap - tap,
3. A - rap - tap - tap, a - rap - tap - tap,
Oh, cob - bler mend my shoe.
Oh, cob - bler see that hole.
The shoe is just like new.
Cobbler A - rap - tap - tap, a - rap - tap - tap,
A - rap - tap - tap, a - rap - tap - tap,
All A - rap - tap - tap, a - rap - tap - tap,
I'll make it just like new.
I'll make a brand new sole.
A ver - y use - ful shoe.

SHOES

1. Win-dows full of shoes, Oh, what fun to choose!
2. Win-dows full of shoes, Oh, what fun to choose!
Shin - y black to wear on Sun - day,
First you have to sit and try them,
Plain - er ones for days like Mon - day,
Next you choose, and then you buy them,
Sturd - y, good new shoes.
Sturd - y, good new shoes.
Let some of us sing this call, while others sing the song.
Shoes, shoes, new shoes, shoes!
SHOE SALE

TAP-A-TAP TAP

Tap - a - tap tap goes the car - pen - ter man,
Tap - a - tap tap goes his ham - mer all day,
He's pound - ing the nails as fast as he can.
In sun - shine or rain he's tap - ping a - way.
Tap - a - tap - a - tap - ping, the car - pen - ter man,
We hear the ham - mer rap - ping as fast as it can.
Let some of us hum, while others sing the song.

THE FIREMAN
Steadily
1. The fire - men are pa - rad - ing,
2. The fire - man's al - ways read - y
3. The fire - man is a sol - dier,
so proud and strong,
by night or day;
so true, so brave,
Oh, I could watch a big pa - rade
If we should have a fire he'd be
He fights the fire in - stead of men,
the whole day long.
there right a - way.
our lives to save.
FIRE

MY PRESENT

Gaily
Moth-er went to town to-day to buy a brand new
dress "For some-one that I love" she said,
Oh, who can it be? Oh, who can it be?
It's for me, it's for me, I guess!
DRESS SHOP
SWISH!
Look out when the wa-ter wag-on sings, "Swish, swish"!

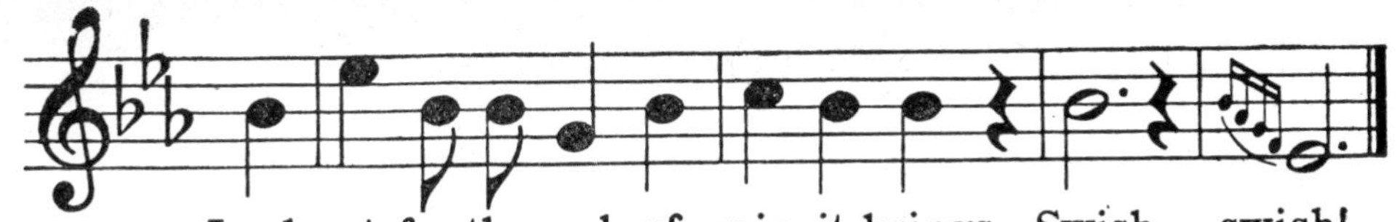
Look out for the rush of rain it brings, Swish, swish!

MY SHOPPING LIST

1. When I go down to Cas-par's shop,
2. And when I ask a - bout the cheese,
3. And when I say I'll have some rice,
4. And when I read my shop-ping list
To buy a loaf and mut - ton chop,
And say "I'll taste it, if you please,"
But want to know the low - est price,
For fear there's some-thing I have missed,
Cas-par says, "Ver - y good to - day."
Cas-par says, "Cer-tain - ly you may."
Cas-par says, "Ver - y cheap to - day."
Cas-par says, "Come a - gain some day."
23¢
4 FOR 5¢
CASP
PROVIS

THE GROCER MAN

SOME OF US
1. I am the gro - cer man!
2. I am the gro - cer man!
OTHERS
Buy of the gro - cer man!
Buy of the gro - cer man!
1st GROUP
Nice po - ta - toes, nice po - ta - toes,
Ripe to - ma - toes, ripe to - ma - toes,
EVERYONE
Nice po - ta - toes to - day!
Ripe to - ma - toes to - day!
10

B

THE JOLLY MILLER

Not too fast
1. To wan-der is the mil-ler's joy, to wan-der,
2. The bus-y mill wheel ev- er turns, the mill wheel,
To wan-der is the mil-ler's joy, to wan-der.
The bus-y mill wheel ev- er turns, the mill wheel.
But while he sings his mer-ry lay,
But still he sings his mer-ry lay,
His heart is o'er the hills a - way,
"My heart is o'er the hills a - way,
f
pp
To wan-der, to wan-der, To wan-der, to wan-der.
To wan-der, to wan-der, To wan-der, to wan-der."

This song was written by Franz Schubert, who began to write tunes when he was a boy.

GOING TO THE CIRCUS

CIRCUS PARADE

1. Here they come! Cir-cus hors-es neigh-ing,
2. See the clowns, Go-ing thro' their pac - es,
Bum! bum! bum! Hear the mu-sic play-ing.
Grins and frowns, Mak-ing fun-ny fac - es.
See the zoo, El - e-phants and ze - bras,
Too-too - too! That's the steam pi - an - o,
Ti - gers, too, The cir - cus is in town!
Now it's through, We might as well go home.

THE CLOWN

1. When the cir - cus comes to town,
2. You should see him jump and skip
3. Now I real - ly do sup - pose
We shall go to see the clown,
When the mas - ter cracks the whip.
That he has a prop - er nose,
He is such a fun - ny sight
In the saw - dust he will sprawl,
If he wash - es off the red
With his face all red and white.
But he is - n't hurt at all.
When it's time to go to bed.

HAVE YOU SEEN THE ZOO?

Not too slowly
1. Have you ev - er seen the zoo?
2. Have you ev - er seen the zoo?
It is quite the thing to do.
It is quite the thing to do.
There are kan - ga - roos and mon - keys,
There are mar - mo - sets and ta - pirs,
There are beasts that look like don - keys,
And the chim - pan - zees cut ca - pers.
There's a cas - so - wa - ry, too,
There are bears and bea - vers, too,
LIONS
SEALS

W

And they all live in the zoo.
And they all live in the zoo.

BIG BROWN BEAR

Big brown bear! How he swings his
bod - y round, How he wags his head!
I should think that he'd be tired, Mov-ing right and
mov-ing left, Big brown bear!

SEE THAT ELEPHANT

1. See that el - e - phant, high and wide;
2. Good old el - e - phant lives on hay,
3. Good - bye, el - e - phant, we must go,
Mount that el - e - phant, take a ride.
Eats a lot of it ev - 'ry day.
Good old el - e - phant, safe and slow.
He will car - ry you care - ful - ly, safe - ly,
Tho' he sure - ly likes pea - nuts and can - dy,
We'll come back a - gain bring - ing you pea - nuts,
Good old el - e - phant, high and wide.
Good old el - e - phant lives on hay.
Good - bye, el - e - phant, we must go.

T

GOING HERE AND THERE IN ALL KINDS OF WEATHER

W
S
E
N
WEATHER VANE
1. Weath - er vane, weath - er vane,
2. Weath - er vane, high up there,
Tell us, will it snow or rain.
Try to make the weath - er fair.
What other kinds of weather shall we ask for?

RAIN OR SHINE

1. The sun-shine is so bright and gay
2. On driz-zly days I stay in-side
It makes me hap-py all the day.
And watch the rain-drops slip and slide.
It keeps me warm from head to toe.
They al-ways seem to have such fun,
I nev-er, nev-er like, nev-er, nev-er like,
And never, never miss, nev-er, nev-er miss,
Nev-er, nev-er like to see it go.
Nev-er, nev-er, nev-er miss the sun.

W

LITTLE WIND

1. Lit-tle wind, lit-tle wind, Blow on the hill - top;
2. Lit-tle wind, lit-tle wind, Blow on the tree - top;
Lit-tle wind, lit-tle wind, Blow on the plain;
Lit-tle wind, lit-tle wind, Blow on the flow'r;
Lit-tle wind, lit-tle wind, Blow in the sun-shine;
Lit-tle wind, lit-tle wind, Blow off the cloud-cap;
Lit-tle wind, lit-tle wind, Blow out the rain.
Lit-tle wind, lit-tle wind, Blow off the show'r.

Do these words sing themselves?

Blow, wind, blow,—
Go, mill, go—

NEW SHOES

Oh, see my new shoes, my love-ly new shoes!

They're made of stout leath-er for all kinds of weath-er,

Oh, see my new shoes, my love-ly new shoes!

THEY'RE USEFUL

1. No one cares for rain-coats, they would glad-ly spare them,
2. Still, when days are cloud-y it is wise to wear them,

SHOES

No one cares for rub-bers when the walks are dry.
Both will come in hand-y when the rain-drops fly.

What tune fits these words?
Drip, drip, raindrops drip!

WHO HAS SEEN THE WIND?

Who has seen the wind?
Nei - ther you nor I;
But when the trees bow down their heads, The
wind is pass - ing by.

Busy winds are out today,
Blowing all the clouds away.

THE TRIM, TRIG TRAILER

1. A trail - er is a house, a snug lit-tle house on
2. A trail - er is a home, wher - ev - er you choose to
wheels. A place to sleep, a place to eat, a
park, With co - sy bunks and win - dow screens and
place to cook your meals. Wher - ev - er your car may
lights for aft - er dark. By moun-tain or lake or
take its way, Wher - ev - er the road may
sand - y shore, Wher - ev - er the road you

wind, — The trim lit - tle, trig lit - tle
find, — The trim lit - tle, trig lit - tle
trail - er goes, trail - ing on be - hind. —
trail - er goes, trail - ing on be - hind. —

Shall we sing this?

Red light, stop the car,
Green light, start it.

THREE BLIND MICE

Three blind mice; Three blind mice;
See how they run! See how they run!
They ran out in front of a mo - tor - car,
Those three lit - tle mice real - ly had good sight,
It honked! but too late, it had gone too far,
But did - n't re-mem-ber the traf - fic light!
It cut off their tails and so there you are!
We're sor - ry, but they were not ver - y bright.
Three blind mice!
GO

OUR SCHOOL BUS

2
2
1. Here comes the big yel-low bus, Mov-ing safe and
2. I like the big yel-low bus, Like the driv-er
slow. Whoa, bus! we'll all get a-board,
too. Whoa, bus! we stand on the curb
Off to school we go. We are read-y, books and all,
Wait-ing here for you. Take our seats and all sit tight,
Wait-ing for your morn-ing call, Whoa, bus! we'll
Wave to moth-er, we're all right. I like the
all get a-board, Off to school we go.
big yel-low bus, Like the driv-er, too.
BUS STOP
SCHOOL BUS

THE DAILY EXPRESS

As fast as possible
1. Click - et - y clack, a - lunk, a - lunk!
2. O - ver the bridge, a - cross the lake,
A train is com - ing, a - chunk, a - chunk;
A mile a min - ute it has to make—
And click - et - y clack a mile a - way;
A ter - ri - ble snake with flam - ing eyes,
ANY VILLE

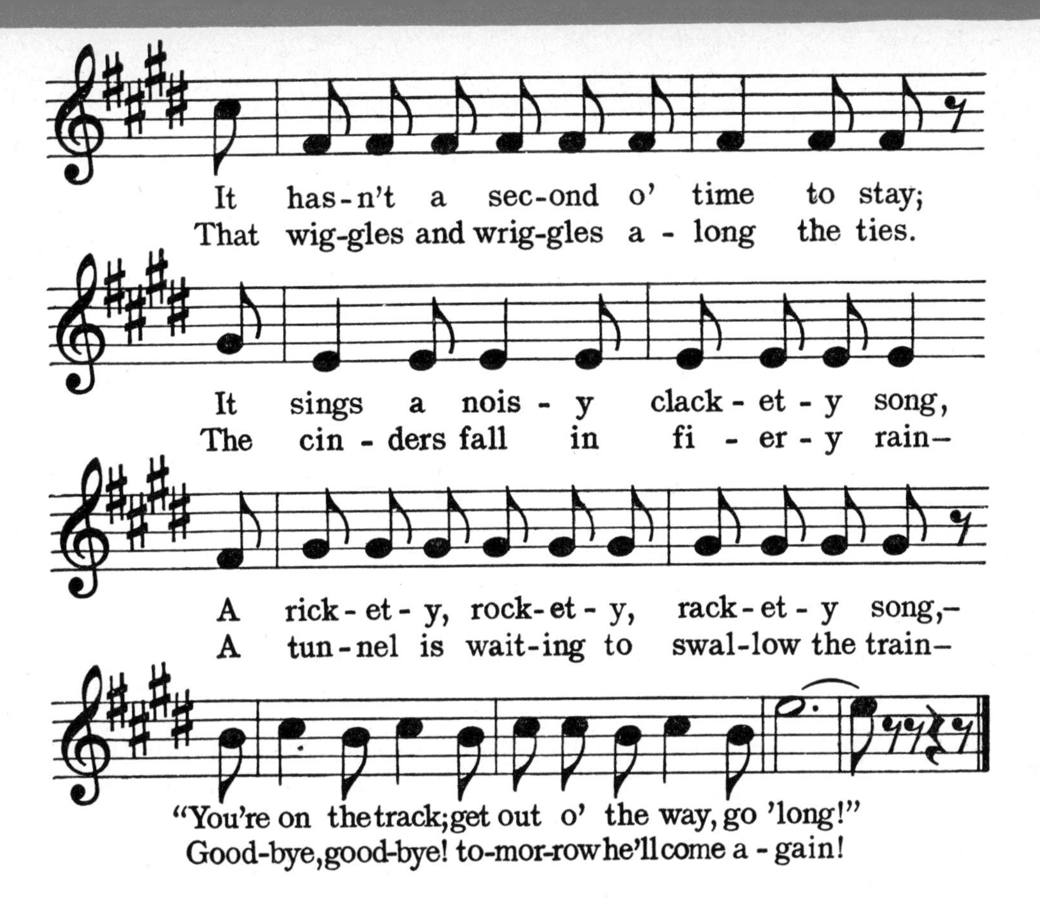
It has-n't a sec-ond o' time to stay;
That wig-gles and wrig-gles a - long the ties.
It sings a nois - y clack - et - y song,
The cin - ders fall in fi - er - y rain–
A rick - et - y, rock- et - y, rack - et - y song,–
A tun - nel is wait-ing to swal-low the train–
"You're on the track; get out o' the way, go 'long!"
Good-bye, good-bye! to-mor-row he'll come a - gain!

Let's sing a tune for this:

Rumble, rumble, rumble goes the elevated train.

THE LINER AND THE TUG

Rather slowly
1 On and on the o-cean lin-er glides;
2. Back a - gain the o-cean lin-er steers;
On and on, a - cross the swell-ing tides.
Back a - gain, to meet our heart - y cheers.
Faster
Far a - way, a - way from you and me. While the
Slow she sails, a - cross the curl-ing foam. While the
fus-sy lit-tle tug keeps puff - ing, puff-ing, puff-ing,
fus-sy lit-tle tug keeps puff - ing, puff-ing, puff-ing,
Till it starts the o-cean lin-er out to sea.
Till it brings the o-cean lin-er safe-ly home.

T

A JOLLY TAR

1. I love to sail up - on the sea,
2. But when I have to play right here,
I love to cross the o - cean.
I sail my mod - el sail - boat.
The sail - or's life's the life for me,
I sail her far, I sail her near,
Oh, I'm a jol - ly tar!
Oh, I'm a jol - ly tar!
Sail, sail,
Little boat, sail.

THE ANT REPORTER

ANT REPORTER
Queen Bee, Queen Bee, I ad-dress your maj-es-ty.
May I have an in-ter-view To ask the bees what
QUEEN BEE (nodding with dignity)
work they do? Zoom— Zoom— Zoom ___
ANT REPORTER (approaching Worker Bees.)
Work-ers, what a-bout your work? What a-bout your work?

INTERVIEWS THE BEES

Brightly
WORKERS
(Hum)
Bus-y, bus-y, al-ways work, Al-ways work, nev-er shirk,
Mak-ing hon-ey all the day, Such good hon-ey.
(Repeat, humming)
ANT REPORTER (surprised)
Queen Bee, Queen Bee, Is that true, your maj-es-ty.
QUEEN BEE (proudly)
Zoom- Zoom- Zoom.

ANT REPORTER (to Drones)
DRONES (slowly)
Drones, drones, what a-bout you? Zoom,
Zoom, we have noth-ing to do.
Slowly
DRONES (yawning)
We rest and we rest, and we do as we please,
For we are the fa-thers of all of the bees!
They say we are i-dle, too la-zy to fly,

(getting slower and slower ______)
And call us the Drones, Tho'we can't tell you why.
ANT REPORTER (shocked)
Queen Bee, Queen Bee, Is this true your maj-es-ty? ______
QUEEN BEE (sadly)
Zoom,– Zoom, Zoom, Zoom. ______
ANT REPORTER (brightly)
Thank you, thank you, now good - night,
All this news I have to write.

BEES (all dancing around Reporter)
Come a-gain and see our home, Hm Hm
Bus-y Cas-tle Hon-ey-comb, Hm
1.
(Repeat, humming)
2.
Hm Hm Hm.

AN INDIAN'S DAY

SUNRISE SONG

Loud
Repeat, softly
Rise, a - rise, a - rise!
The dawn is here, day is call-ing thee, The
dawn is here, ev - er call-ing thee. Might - y
Day God, he is watch-ing thee, Might - y Life God,
Loud
Repeat, softly
he is guard-ing thee. Rise, a - rise, a - rise!

HY-YA-HO

1. Light our hearts and gay, To the fields we make our way, While the winds a-bout us play,
2. Light our hearts and gay, As we home-ward make our way, While the winds a-bout us play,
Sing-ing as we go, Hy - ya hy - ya hy - ya ho! Hy - ya, hy - ya, hy - ya ho!
Hy - ya ho! ho! Hy - ya ho!
W

SONG OF THE CORN

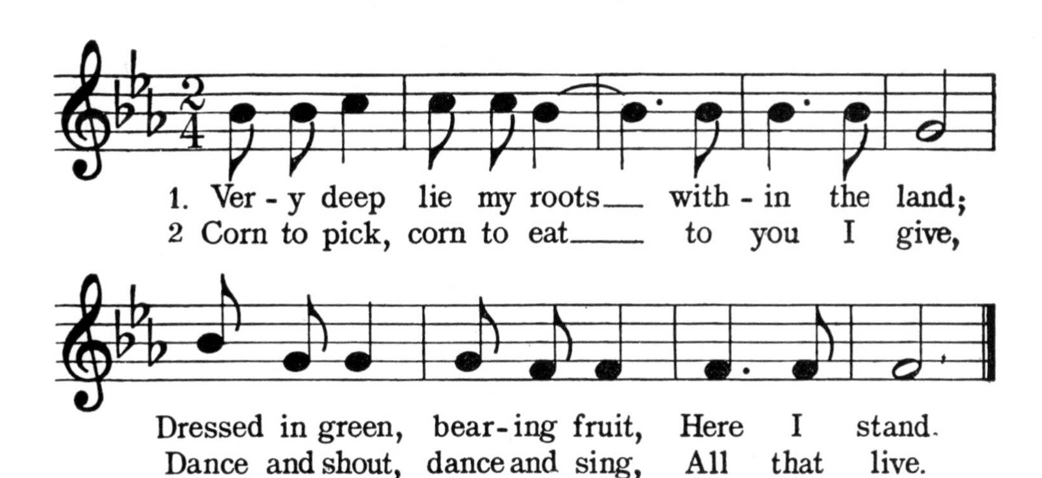
1. Ver - y deep lie my roots___ with - in the land;
2 Corn to pick, corn to eat___ to you I give,
Dressed in green, bear-ing fruit, Here I stand.
Dance and shout, dance and sing, All that live.

FOLLOW MY LEADER

Fol - low my lead - er wher - e'er he goes;
Where he'll take us no - bod - y knows.

SMOKING THE PEACE PIPE
1. We of-fer the peace pipe, we beg you to smoke it,
2. We hon-or your lead-ers, we hon-or your peo-ple,
For now we will be friends, we will be broth-ers.
And now they are our friends, they are our broth-ers.
Take this and smoke it, 'Tis the pipe of peace.

LULLABY

1. Lit - tle ba - by sleep,
2. Way, way, way, way, way,
Moth - er swings your ham - mock low,
Way, way, way, way, way, way, way,
Lit-tle birds rest with - in the nest.
Way, way, way, way, way, way, way, way.

As she swings the hammock, the Chippewa mother sings, "Way, way, way", which is part of the Chippewa word that means "swinging".

7 8 9

AROUND THE CALENDAR

SING A SONG OF SEASONS

Sing a song of sea - sons, Some-thing bright in all,

Flow - ers in the Sum - mer, Fires in the Fall.

IN FOURTEEN HUNDRED NINETY-TWO

1. In four - teen hun - dred nine - ty - two
2. He kept on sail - ing toward the west
Co - lum - bus sailed the o - cean blue;
And nev - er thought of tak - ing rest;
His ship was small but he was brave,
To our great land at last he came,
He dared the wind, he dared the wave.
And so we sing his fa - mous name.

GRAY SQUIRREL

1 & 2. Gray squir-rel, gray squir-rel, whisk your bush-y tail,
Gray squir - rel, gray squir - rel, whisk your bush-y tail.
Wrin - kle up your fun - ny nose,
I will be a friend to you,
Hold the nut be - tween your toes,
So you must be friend - ly, too,
Gray squir-rel, gray squir-rel, whisk your bush-y tail.

B

JACK O'LANTERN

1. Here comes a Jack - o' - lan - tern
2. His head is round and yel - low
With a can - dle for a light,
And his eyes are shin - y bright,
I think he wants to fright - en us
But still he can - not fright - en us
On Hal - low - e'en night.
On Hal - low - e'en night.

IN A HICKORY NUT

A wee lit - tle worm in a hick - o - ry - nut
Sang hap - py as hap - py could be,
"Oh, I live in the heart of a whole round world,
Faster
And it all be-longs to me!"

MINCE PIE

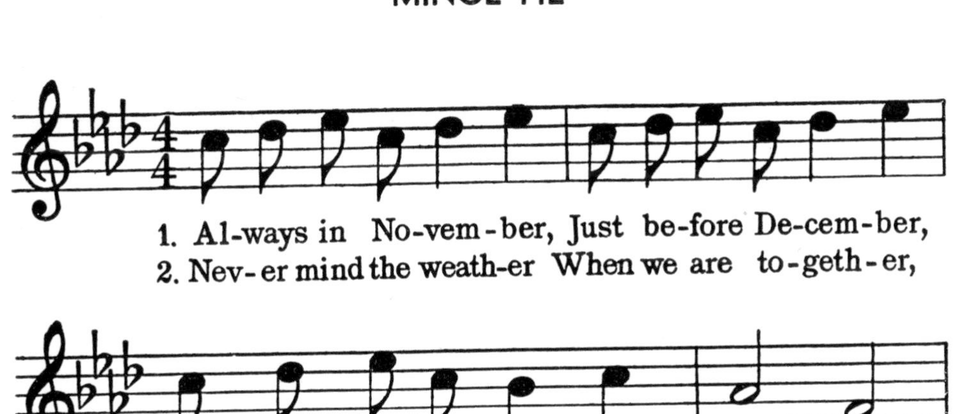
1. Al-ways in No-vem-ber, Just be-fore De-cem-ber,
2. Nev-er mind the weath-er When we are to-geth-er,

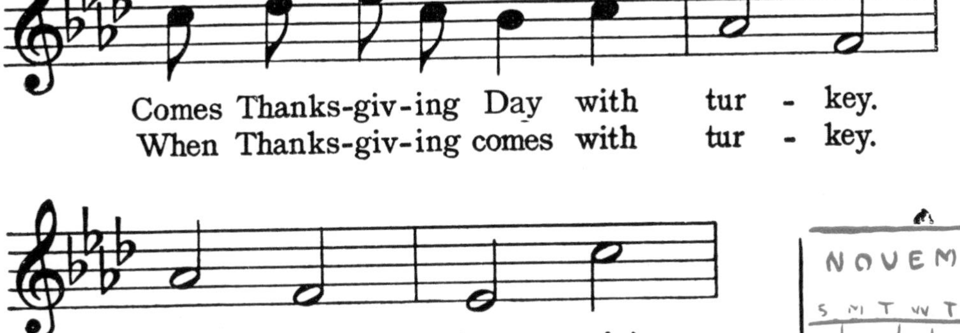
Comes Thanks-giv-ing Day with tur - key.
When Thanks-giv-ing comes with tur - key.

Oh, my, mince pie!
Ev-'ry-bod-y likes mince pie.
NOVEMBER
S M T W T F S

WE GIVE THANKS

Spoken: To the lumbermen who fell the trees to make timber for our houses:

Sung:

We give thanks and for them we ask Thy blessing, Lord.

Spoken: To the miners who dig the coal that keeps us warm:

Sung (as above): We give thanks, etc.

Spoken: To the farmers who plant and reap that we may have food:

Sung: We give thanks, etc.

Spoken: To parents, teachers, and all who work to make our lives beautiful and good:

Sung: We give thanks, etc.

Some of us may hum this descant while others sing the music. Perhaps someone can play it.

T

CHRISTMAS HOLLY

Not too fast

1. Each bright crim-son ber - ry brings mes - sage so
2. While car - ols are ring-ing, the chil - dren are

mer - ry Of hol - ly,___ of hol - ly;___
bring-ing Bright hol - ly,___ bright hol - ly;___

Like can - dles they're shin-ing, in wreaths they are
Its ber - ries are flam-ing, the sea - son pro -

twin-ing, Just hol - ly,___ just hol - ly.___
claim-ing; That's hol - ly,___ that's hol - ly.___

OUR CHRISTMAS PIE

1. What can be in our Christ - mas Pie,
2. Meat and ap - ples and spice, say I,
3. We are jol - ly as we can be,
Christ - mas Pie, Christ - mas Pie,
Spice, say I, spice, say I,
We can be, we can be,
What can be in our Christ - mas Pie,
Meat and ap - ples and spice, say I,
We are jol - ly as we can be,
On Christ - mas Day in the morn - ing?
On Christ - mas Day in the morn - ing.
On Christ - mas Day in the morn - ing.

W

WINTER

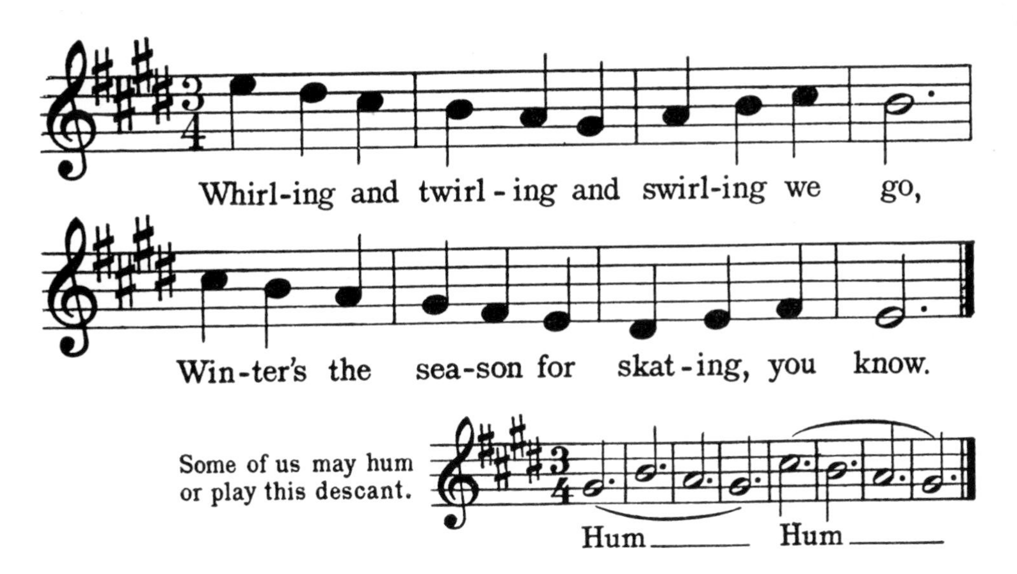
Whirl-ing and twirl - ing and swirl-ing we go,
Win-ter's the sea-son for skat - ing, you know.
Some of us may hum
or play this descant.
Hum Hum

DOWN AND BACK

SOME OF US
1. "Tom - my, Tom-my, Where did you go?"
2. "Tom - my, Tom-my, How was the track?"
OTHERS
"I was coast-ing, coast-ing, Out in the snow."
"It was two miles down hill, Sev-en miles back."

A WONDERFUL MAN OF SNOW

1. I'm a great big man of snow,
2. I have two black coals for eyes,
With a broom-stick gun, ho, ho!
And a pipe that is a prize.
I was rolled down the hill With a laugh and a spill,
With a pan for a hat And a coat and cra-vat,
I'm a won-der-ful man of snow, ho, ho,
I'm a won-der-ful man of snow.

TWO VALENTINES

1. Sing hey! for a val-en-tine, Gay lit-tle val-en-tine,
2. Sing heigh! for a val-en-tine, I sent a val-en-tine,

One that real-ly has my name and my ad-dress.
One that said, "A val-en-tine from me to you."

Sing heigh! for a val-en-tine, My lit-tle val-en-tine,
Sing ho! for a val-en-tine, Oh, for a val-en-tine,

ST.
VALENT

I can tell you where it's from with just one guess.
Some-one got the one I sent, I won't say who.

YANKEE DOODLE

Oh, Yan-kee Doo-dle came to town A - rid-ing on a
po - ny, He stuck a feath - er in his hat And
called it mac - a - ro - ni. Yan - kee Doo - dle
keep it up, Yan-kee Doo-dle dan-dy, Mind the mu-sic
and the step And with the girls be han - dy.

This song was sung in George Washington's time.

MINUET

This tune was written by Wolfgang Mozart, who began to write tunes when he was four years old. He lived at the same time as George Washington, and the minuet was danced then.

The tune may be hummed while we dance, or we may write our own words.

MISS CHICKADEE
1. My dear Miss Chick-a-dee, I'm ver - y fond of you;
2. My dear Miss Chick-a-dee, I'll sing my sweet-est tune
Won't you please mar-ry me When skies are clear and blue.
If you will mar-ry me When ros - es come in June.
Repeat, softly
See, see, my home is made for two.
See, see, my home is made for two.
GROWING
1. Oh, the ground looks dark and the ground looks brown,
2. Oh, the roots grow strong and the stems grow stout,
But the seeds are all a - wak-ing and the roots go down.
All the chil-dren are de-light-ed when a plant pops out.

MARCH WIND

1. Blow - ing, blow - ing, Oo! ___
2. Blow - ing, blow - ing, Oo! ___
The wind of March blows down the hill,
It blows the win - ter clouds a - way,
And through the val - ley, too.
And leaves the shin - ing blue.
WINTER'S GOING
1. Win - ter's go - ing, mild wind blow - ing,
2. Blue-bird bright and Rob - in Red-breast
Soon comes A - pril weath - er.
Soon will sing to - geth - er.

SAINT PATRICK'S DAY

Gaily
1. We're hap - py to - day and we'll join in the sing-ing
2. The sham-rock ap-pears and the green flag is fly - ing,
A live - ly old tune that is jol - ly and gay;
With Ta - ra's gold harp it is lead - ing the way;
The peo - ple pa - rade and the bells are all ring-ing,
The mu - sic of bands and the ech - oes re - ply - ing
For folks will turn out on Saint Pat-rick's Day.
U- nite in the song of Saint Pat-rick's Day.

EASTER TIME

1. The lit - tle flow'rs peeped thro' the ground
2. "We hear the song of heav'n to - day,"
At Eas - ter time, at Eas - ter time,
Each love - ly blos - som seemed to say,
They raised their heads and looked a - round
"Good peo - ple, sing with joy and pray
At hap - py, hap - py Eas - ter time.
That God will bless each Eas - ter Day."

SPRING GREETING

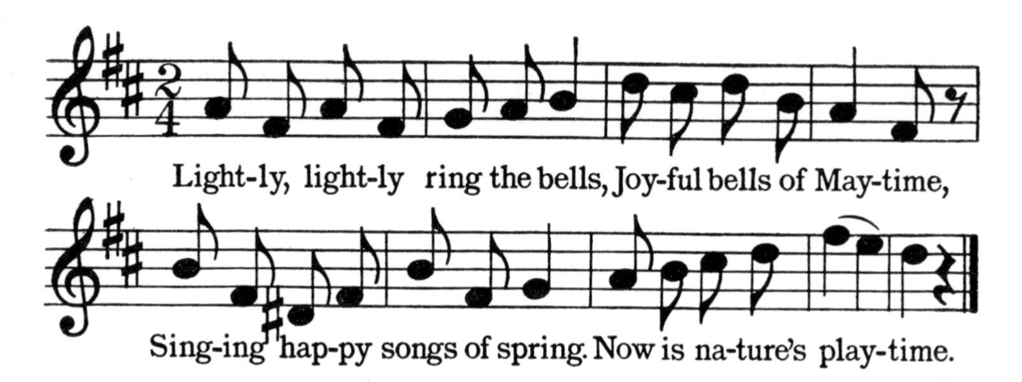
Light-ly, light-ly ring the bells, Joy-ful bells of May-time,
Sing-ing hap-py songs of spring. Now is na-ture's play-time.

This song was written by Felix Mendelssohn, who played the piano in public when he was only nine years old.

THE HURDY-GURDY MAN

1. Hur- ry, scur- ry, scam-per, Fast as you can,
2. When he plays a pol - ka, Dance if you can,
Just a-round the cor-ner is the hur-dy-gur-dy man.
Then we'll give a pen-ny to the hur-dy-gur-dy man.

MOTHER'S DAY

1. Moth-er dear, I sing to you on Moth-er's Day.
2. Moth-er dear, there's one thing more I'd like to say—
This is my song—I love you, yes I do!
I'm ver-y glad that I be-long to you!

BUTTERCUPS, TOO

1. I like flow-ers, don't you? Pink or yel-low or blue;
2. I like ros-es, don't you? Ros-es spark-ling with dew;
Pan-sies, hol-ly-hocks, and I like but-ter-cups, too.
Lil-ies, daf-fo-dils, and I like but-ter-cups, too.

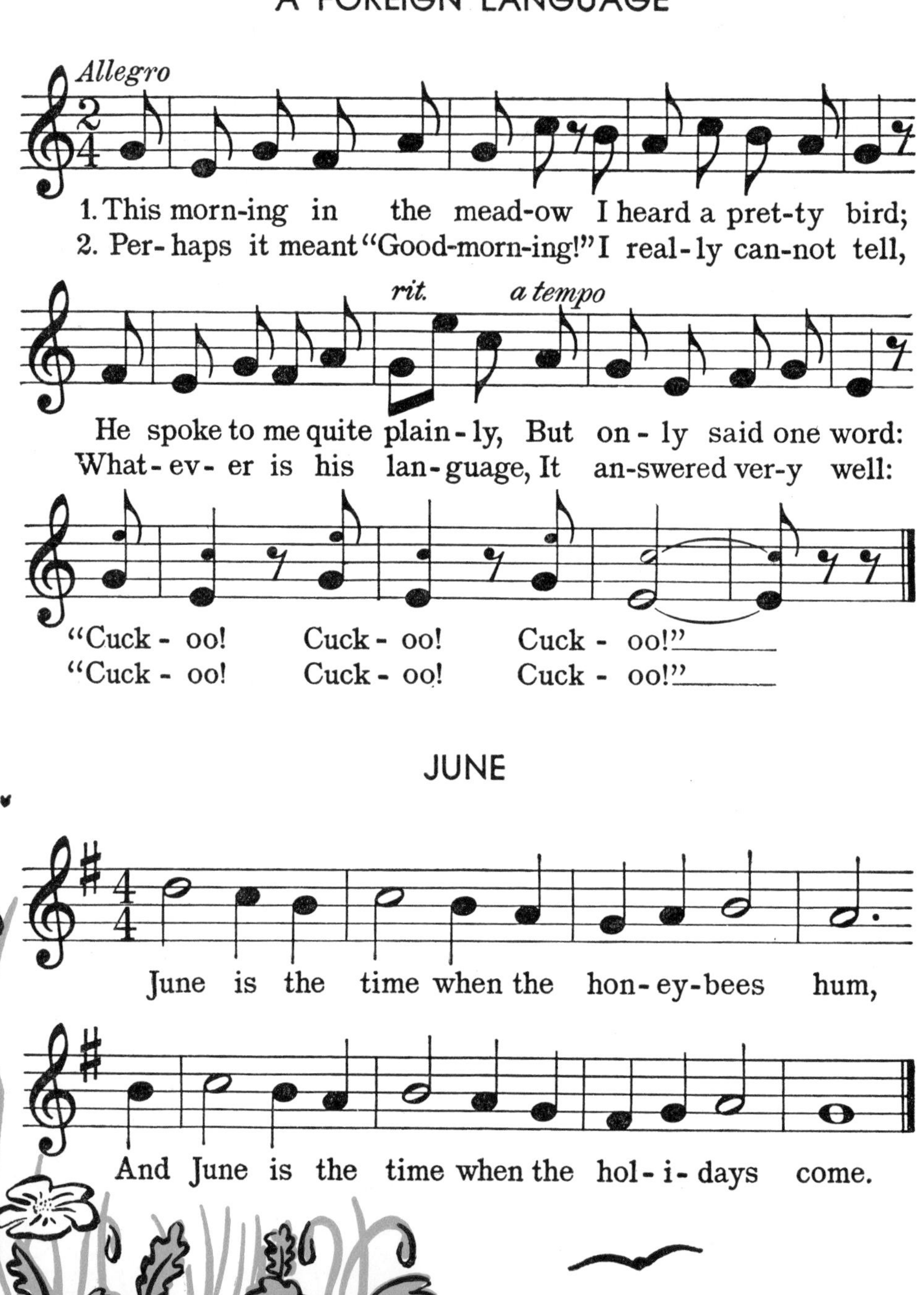
A FOREIGN LANGUAGE
Allegro
1. This morn-ing in the mead-ow I heard a pret-ty bird;
2. Per-haps it meant "Good-morn-ing!" I real-ly can-not tell,
rit.
a tempo
He spoke to me quite plain-ly, But on-ly said one word:
What-ev-er is his lan-guage, It an-swered ver-y well:
"Cuck-oo! Cuck-oo! Cuck-oo!"
"Cuck-oo! Cuck-oo! Cuck-oo!"
JUNE
June is the time when the hon-ey-bees hum,
And June is the time when the hol-i-days come.

WHEN BANDS BEGIN TO PLAY

1. When the bands be - gin to play
2. When the bands be - gin to play
3. When the bands be - gin to play,
On our na - tion's hol - i - day,
We will march in brave ar - ray,
"For - ward march!" the lead - ers say,
We will sing a song and march a - long,
With our eyes a - head and stead - y tread,
And a - way we go with hearts a - glow,
When bands be - gin to play.
When bands be - gin to play.
When bands be - gin to play.
Rub-a-dub-dub

THE WAVES AND I

Brightly
1. I play a game of tag,
2. But when the tide goes out,
In sum - mer on the beach,
I'm brave as I can be,
And when the waves run aft - er me,
For then I chase the sau - cy waves,
Faster
I run far out of reach.
And send them back to sea.

SUMMER LULLABY

Quietly
1. All through the night The sum-mer moon was bright.
2. I fell a - sleep While he was say - ing "Cheep."
Crick - et gave a ser - e - nade,
I en - joyed his mu - sic, but—
Just a sin - gle note he played,
Next I knew, my eyes were shut.
All through the night.
I fell a - sleep.

WE SING, PLAY AND DANCE

Music land, music land,
Where we dance,
Where we play,
Where we sing with the band.

A STATELY DANCE

1. Let us dance to - geth - er, Bow-ing as we go,
2. Crin-o-lines a - sway-ing, Mu - sic soft and low,
Let us dance the min-u - et, So state - ly and so slow.
When we dance the min-u - et By light of can-dle-glow.

I'M LEARNING TO DANCE

1. I'm learn-ing to dance and it's oh, so much fun,
2. I'm learn-ing to sing and it's oh, so much fun,
Oh, so much fun, oh, so much fun,
Oh, so much fun, oh, so much fun,
I'm learn-ing to dance and it's oh, so much fun,
I'm learn-ing to sing and it's oh, so much fun,
I'll soon dance a dance just for you.
I'll soon learn a song just for you.

A GAY LITTLE DANCE

1. O hey-did-dle-did-dle, The cat plays a tune;
2. O hey-did-dle-did-dle, The cat plays a tune;
See the cow jump O-ver the moon.
See the gay dish Skip with the spoon.
O hey-did-dle-did-dle, Oh, we can jump, too,
O hey-did-dle-did-dle, Oh, we can skip, too,
Ho! Ho! Hey-did-dle-doo!
Ho! Ho! Hey-did-dle-doo!

SO-SOW-SEWING

1. Shall I show you how the farm - er,
2. It is *so*, *so*, that the farm - er,
3. Shall I show you how the tail - or,
4. It is *so*, *so*, that the tail - or,
Shall I show you how the farm - er,
It is *so*, *so*, that the farm - er,
Shall I show you how the tail - or,
It is *so*, *so*, that the tail - or,
Shall I show you how the farm - er
It is *so*, *so*, that the farm - er
Shall I show you how the tail - or
It is *so*, *so*, that the tail - or
Sows his bar - ley and wheat?
Sows his bar - ley and wheat.
Sews a ver - y fine seam?
Sews a ver - y fine seam.

SPANISH DANCE

What instruments can we play to make this music sound Spanish?

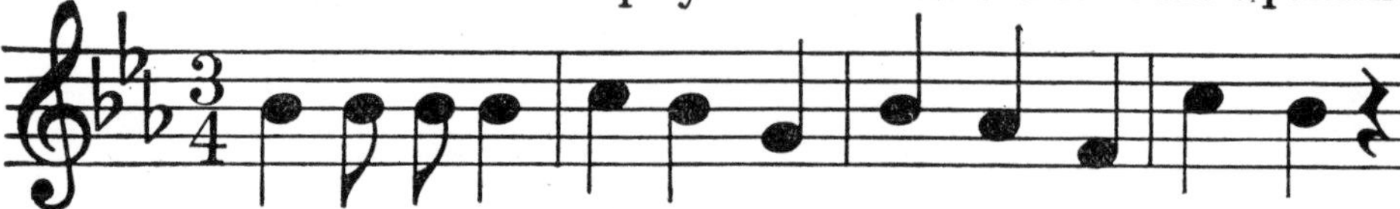

1. Tra- la-la-la - la - la, We're danc-ing to - geth - er,
2. Tra- la-la-la - la - la, In all kinds of weath-er,

Tra - la-la-la - la - la, A gay whirl-ing waltz.
Tra - la-la-la - la - la, We sing as we waltz.

WE SING AS WE MARCH

What instruments shall we play with this music?

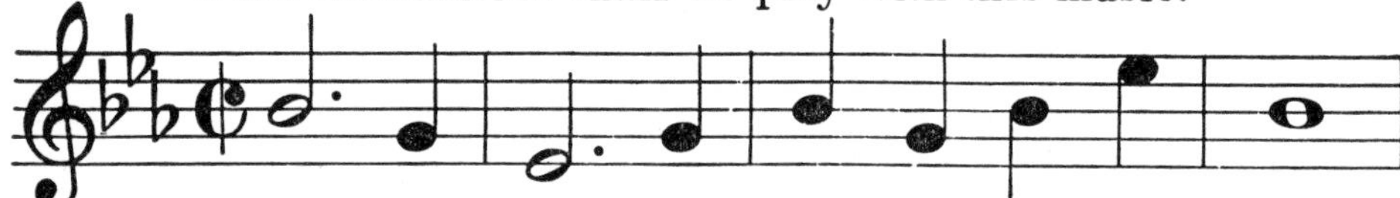

1. Hark, oh, hark! The trum-pet seems to say,
2. Hark, oh, hark! The drums will loud - ly beat,

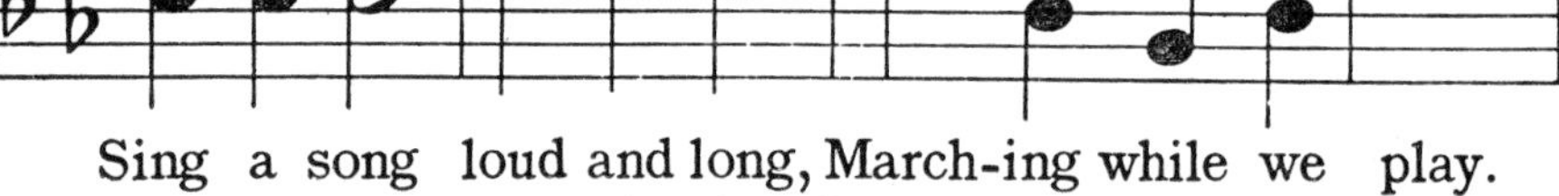

Sing a song loud and long, March-ing while we play.
So we sing, voic-es ring, March-ing down the street.

Left, right, left, right, marching right along,
Left, right, left, right, marching to a song.

THE TRIANGLE

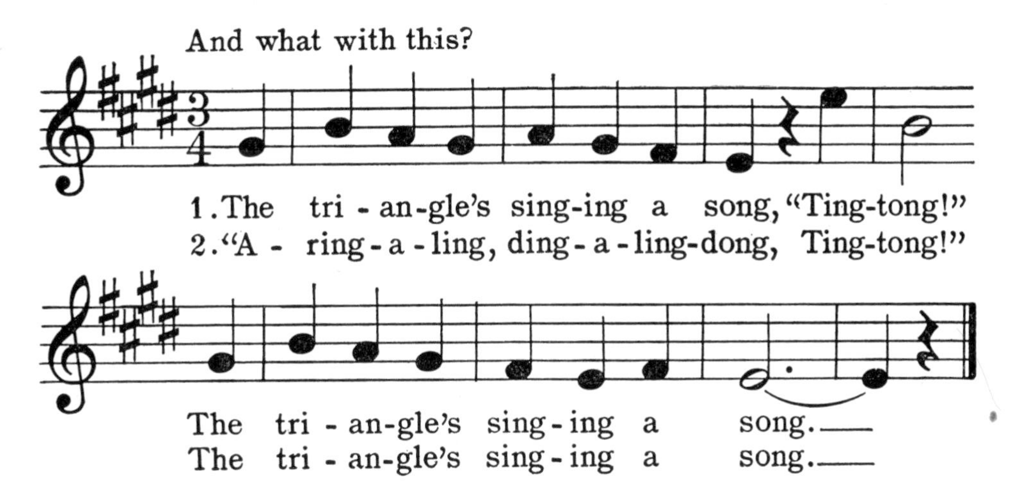
And what with this?
1. The tri - an-gle's sing-ing a song, "Ting-tong!"
2. "A - ring - a - ling, ding - a - ling-dong, Ting-tong!"
The tri - an-gle's sing - ing a song.
The tri - an-gle's sing - ing a song.

JINGLE BELLS

And what with this?
Jin - gle bells, jin - gle bells, jin - gle all the
way, Oh, what fun it is to ride in a
1.
one horse o - pen sleigh!
2.
one horse o - pen sleigh!

HIPPITY HOP

Hip - pi - ty hop, Hip - pi - ty hop,
I know a girl who nev - er could stop;
She hip - pi - ty hopped both here and there,
She hip - pi - ty hopped 'most ev - 'ry - where,
I've oft - en, oft - en, heard it said,

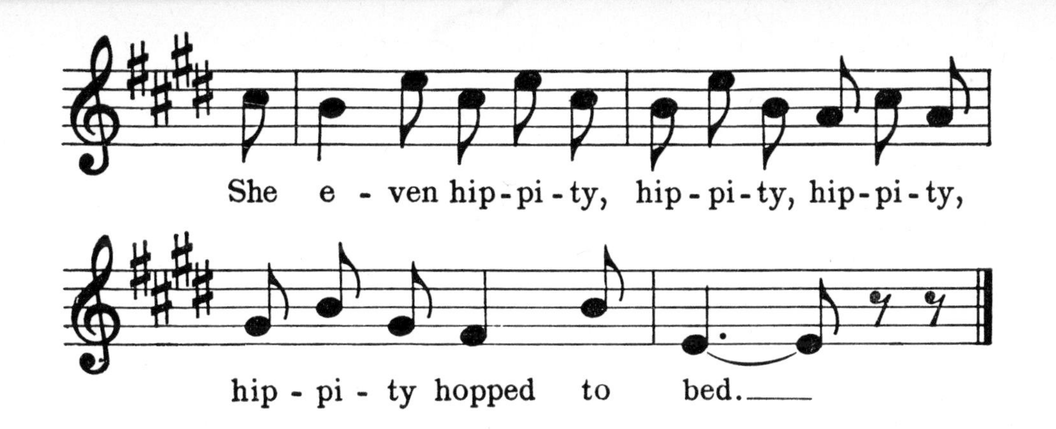
She e - ven hip - pi - ty, hip - pi - ty, hip - pi - ty,
hip - pi - ty hopped to bed.

A DUET

(Child) The waves are roll - ing down the shore, Roll, roll, roll, roll,
(Waves) Sh - sh - sh - sh, sh, sh, sh, sh,
The waves are leap - ing o'er and o'er, Roll, roll, roll.
Sh - sh - sh - sh, sh, sh, sh.

SWINGING
Swing high, swing low,
High in the air we mer-ri-ly go,
Up in the trees we play with the breeze,
And fly with the birds as we're swing-ing.

ON THE VILLAGE GREEN

1. Dance with me, my sweet Ma - rie,
2. Tra la la la la la la,
Up - on the vil - lage green, O,
Tra la la la la la lo,
All the day we'll laugh and play,
Tra la la la la la la,
And you shall be the queen, O.
Tra la la la la la lo.

Tra, la, la, la, Tra la, lo.

MY FIDDLE
Quietly
Draw the bow a - cross the strings, Hm
Lis-ten as my fid-dle sings, Hm
TWO FRIENDS
Bird: Swing, swing, lit - tle one swing,
Child: Fly, fly, fly to the sky,
Mer-ri - ly swing and sing.
Mer-ri - ly sing and fly.

285 Columbus Ave.,
Boston, Mass.

Dear Boys and Girls:

When you are playing do you ever hear a nice "dancey" tune running through your head? I do, and sometimes I like my tunes a lot. Here are some words and a tune that were written by boys and girls of your age.

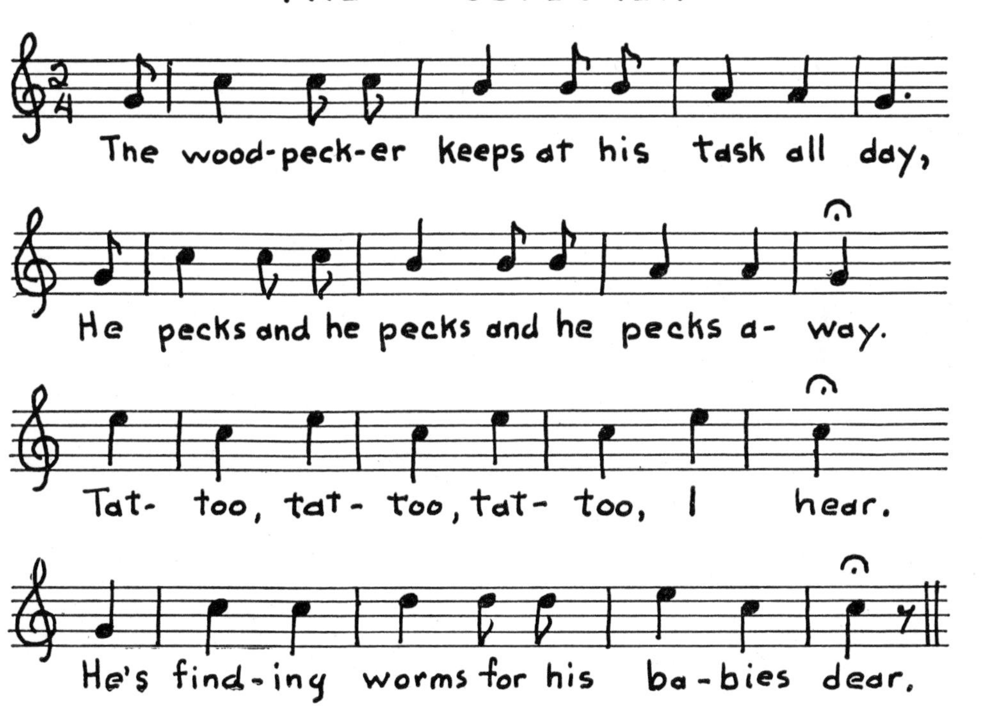
THE WOODPECKER
The wood-peck-er keeps at his task all day,
He pecks and he pecks and he pecks a- way.
Tat- too, tat - too, tat- too, I hear.
He's find-ing worms for his ba-bies dear.

Why don't you try making your own tunes—and words, too, about things that you like?

When you read these words, "By low by, baby bye," don't they sing a tune to you? And these: "Rub a dub dub, three men in a tub!" And these: Everybody now-a-days
Seems in such a hurry
Why-oh-why
All this hurry-scurry?"

If you think of a very good song, sing it over and over. Make sure you have it just the way you want it. Perhaps someone will help you write it down. Then you can always remember it. If you make a <u>very</u> good song and get it nicely written down, please send it to me. I would like to see it.

Yours,
Tuneful Tim
c/o C. C. Birchard Co.

P.S. If you look, you will find verses on some of the pages of this book. Perhaps you will make tunes for them.
T. T.

THE MUSIC ROAD

There's a road through music land,
With a song in every tree,
And little notes that run and skip
Along the way with me.

YOO-HOO

SOME OF US
"Yoo - hoo, yoo - hoo" Ma-ry's call-ing "Yoo-hoo,"
OTHERS
"Yoo - hoo, yoo - hoo" Bob-by's call-ing back.

SONGS FOR STUDY

A MUSICAL MIX-UP
1. Sup-pose all the bird-ies read songs from a book,
2. Sup-pose all the chil-dren sat up in a tree,
3. But birds need the tree-top, and want their own song,
And sang all the tunes with a ver-y wise look,
And sang like the bird-ies a twit-ter chee chee,
And we need to stay where all chil-dren be-long,
Sing-ing do mi so fa mi re do.
Not this do mi so fa mi re do.
Sing-ing do mi so fa mi re do.

THE BIG, BIG SKY
I can see the big, big sky,
blue and high.

SUN AND MOON

I see the sun, I see the sun,
The sun is hot, the sun is gold.
I see the moon, I see the moon,
The moon is white, the moon is cold.

STAR

Star, star, star! Star, star, star!
I can see you wink, wink, wink,
I can see you blink, blink, blink,
Star, star, star!

STORM CLOUDS
One cloud, two clouds, Crash! Crash! Crash!
Zis! Zis! Flash! Flash! Flash!
One cloud, two clouds, Bump! Bump! Bump!
Bang! Bang! Thump! Thump! Thump!

RAINBOW

Rain - bow, rain - bow, you are so plain,
Now I am sure there will be no more rain.
Rain - bow, rain - bow, up in the blue;
Now I can play for the sun has come through.

LITTLE BLACK CAT

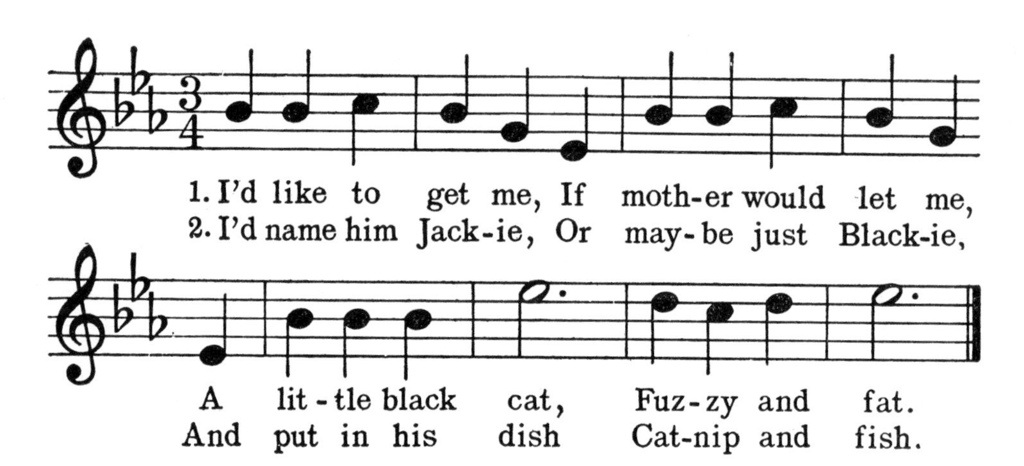
1. I'd like to get me, If moth-er would let me,
2. I'd name him Jack-ie, Or may-be just Black-ie,
A lit-tle black cat, Fuz-zy and fat.
And put in his dish Cat-nip and fish.

TWILIGHT

Some of Us
Others
Twi-light bells are soft-ly ring-ing, Ding, dong, ding, dong.
First Group
Second Group
Sleep-y songs we all are sing-ing, Sing, song, sing, song.

GOOD MORNING, WE SAY

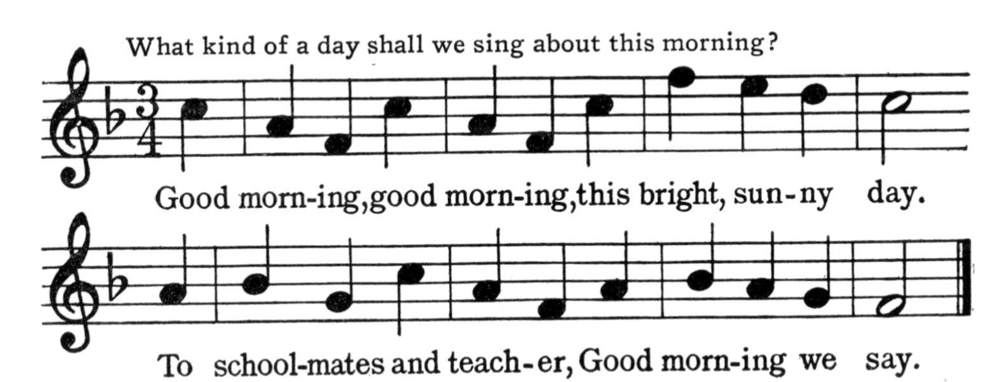
What kind of a day shall we sing about this morning?
Good morn-ing, good morn-ing, this bright, sun-ny day.
To school-mates and teach-er, Good morn-ing we say.

THANKSGIVING

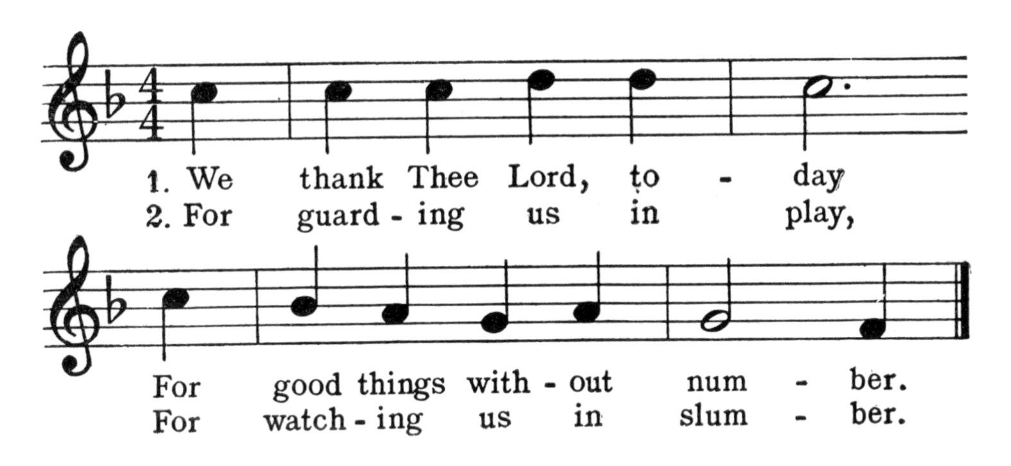
1. We thank Thee Lord, to - day
2. For guard - ing us in play,
For good things with - out num - ber.
For watch - ing us in slum - ber.

CHINESE NEW YEAR

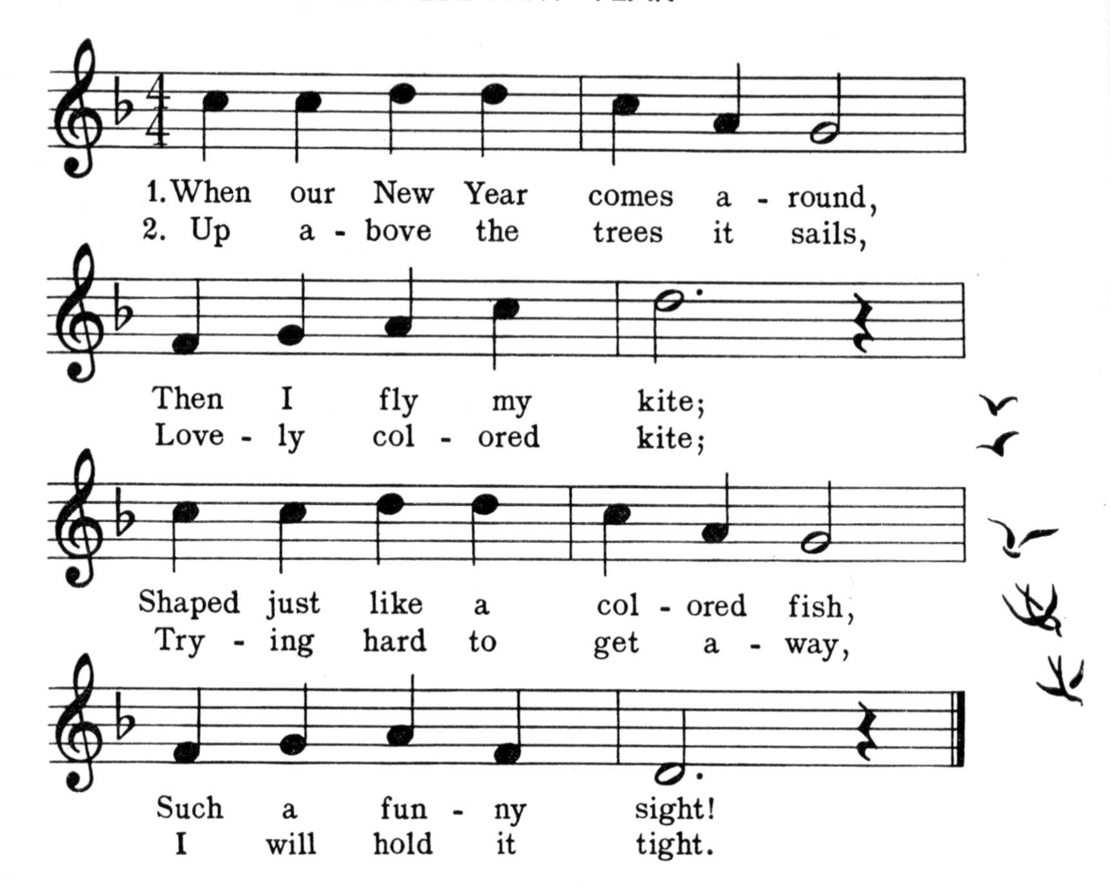
1. When our New Year comes a - round,
2. Up a - bove the trees it sails,
Then I fly my kite;
Love - ly col - ored kite;
Shaped just like a col - ored fish,
Try - ing hard to get a - way,
Such a fun - ny sight!
I will hold it tight.

BABY, SLEEP

French mothers sing this song to their children.

Sleep, sleep, ba-by sleep; Soon my lit-tle one will sleep.

STREAMLINE TRAINS
Not too fast
1. When I go a - way a - gain, I
2. Stream-line trains go whizz - ing past, They
Faster
think that I will trav - el on a stream-line train.
look like fly - ing ar - rows when they go so fast.
SLEEPY SONG
See the sandman, here he comes bringing slum-ber sand;
Close your drow-sy eyes and go off to Sleep-y Land.

LET'S SING THESE SONGS ALL BY OURSELVES

SEESAW

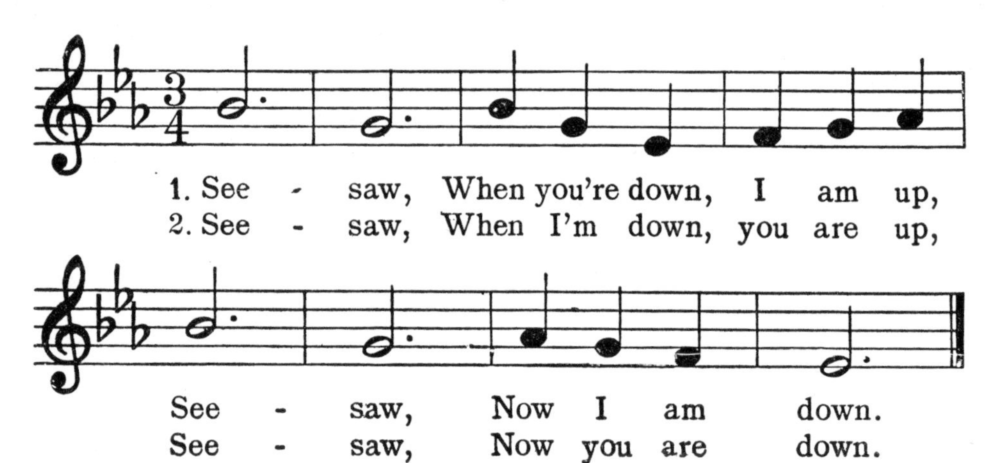
1. See - saw, When you're down, I am up,
2. See - saw, When I'm down, you are up,
See - saw, Now I am down.
See - saw, Now you are down.

HIGH, LOW

High, low, high, low,
Reach-ing so high, bend-ing so low.
UPS AND DOWNS
Swing-ing up so high I go,

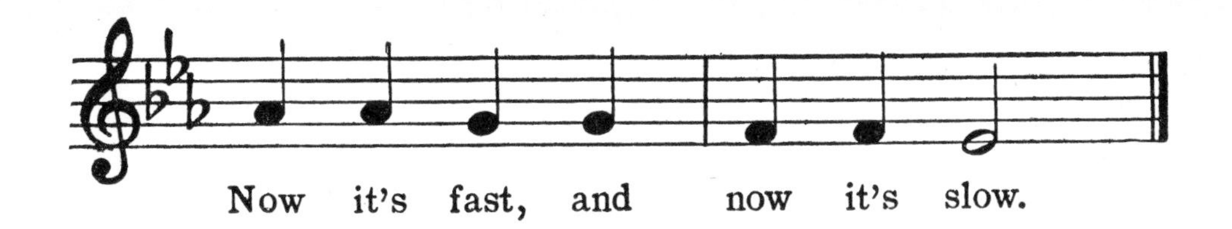
Now it's fast, and now it's slow.

SLUMBER SONG

Sleep on moth-er's arm, By - low, by - low,
Have no fear of harm, By - low, by - low.

LIGHTNING BUG

Light - ning bug, Flash your light,
Show me where to walk to - night.

WANDERING

1. I will go some pleas - ant day,
2. O'er the hills and far a - way,
Here and there and yon - der.
I would like to wan - der.

BAND MUSIC

1. Rub! Dub! Stead - y beat,
2. Left! Right! Here they come,
Men are march - ing down the street.
How I like to play the drum.

A LONG TRIP

1. Jer - ry and Jim - my went off to sea
2. Jer - ry and Jim - my a - way from school

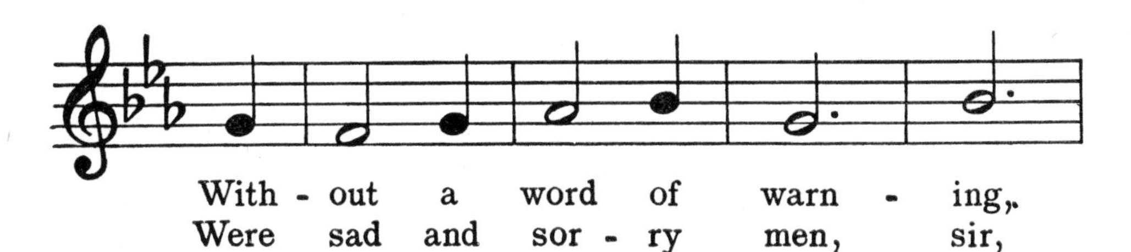

With - out a word of warn - ing,
Were sad and sor - ry men, sir,

Start - ed a - way on the stroke of three
Head - ed for home as the clock struck four,

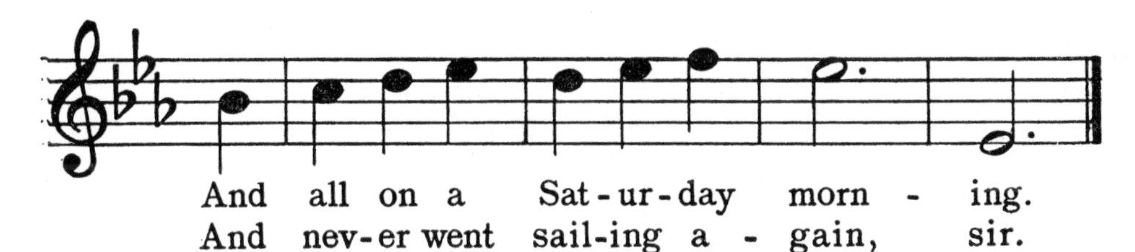

And all on a Sat - ur - day morn - ing.
And nev - er went sail - ing a - gain, sir.

THE WHALE

BUGLE, BLOW

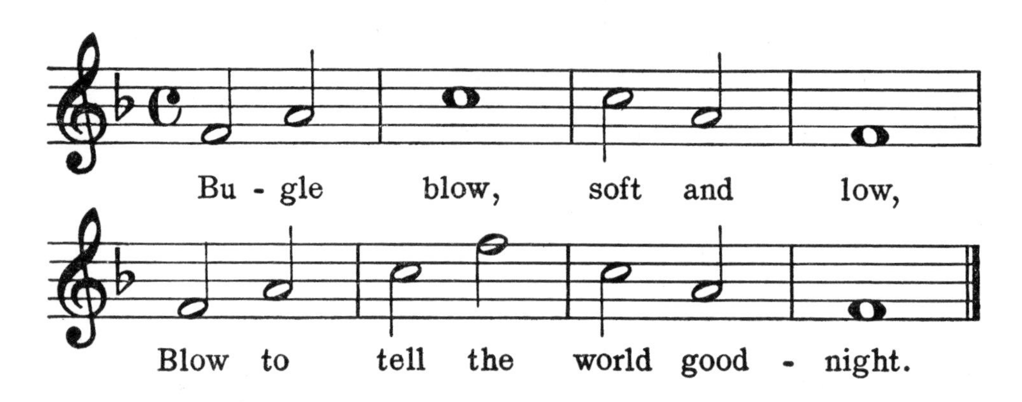
Bu - gle blow, soft and low,
Blow to tell the world good - night.

NIGHT WINDS

p 1. Night winds blow soft - ly, Flow'rs now close their eyes.
2. Soft glow of star-light Fills the ev-'ning skies.

HOW THEY GROW

1. Oats and beans and corn and bar - ley,
2. Sun and rain and sum - mer weath - er,

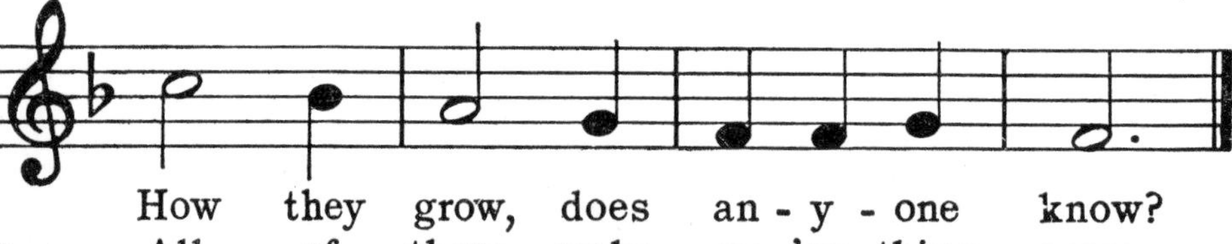
How they grow, does an - y - one know?
All of these make ev-'ry-thing grow.

NEW SIMPLE SIMON

1. Sim - ple Si - mon, one fine day,
2. Si - mon said, "I'll have a pie,
3. "Nay, my lad," the pie - man said,
4. Si - mon, to my great sur - prise,
One fine day, one fine day,
Have a pie, have a pie,
Pie - man said, pie - man said,
Great sur - prise, great sur - prise,
Met a pie - man on his way,
That big fat one I will try,
"You must pay be - fore you're fed,
Showed his purse and bought two pies,
Sell - ing good pies.
Those are good pies."
Those are my pies."
Ver - y good pies.

THINGS THAT GO FAST OR SLOW

A BUSY CLOCK

Not too fast
1. Tick, tock, tick, tock, tick, tock, tick, tock,
2. Tick, tock, tick, tock, tick, tock, tick, tock,
Our big clock is say - ing,
Ev - en while we're play - ing.
Tick, tock, tick, tock, tick, tock, tick, tock,
Tick, tock, tick, tock, tick, tock, tick, tock,
While the min-utes creep.
While we're all a - sleep.
Some of us may hum this descant.
Hum

T

MY DADDY'S WATCH

Does the music show that the watch ticks faster than the clock?

First verse, very fast
Second verse, slow until the last measure
1. My dad - dy's watch says, "Tick, tick, tick, tick,
2. Some - times it stops its tick, tick, tick, tick,
tick, tick, tick, tick, tock;"
tick, tick, tick, tick, tock;
It says a hap - py tick, tick, tick, tick,
When dad - dy winds it, then it goes tick,
tick, tick, tick, tick, tock.
tick, tick, tick, tick, tock.

WAVES

Slowly
Fall - ing, ris - ing, fall - ing, ris - ing,
O - cean waves for - ev - er go.
Faster
Now the storm - y clouds are form - ing,
Wild - er now the wa - ters grow.
Dreamily
Now the gold - en sun is sink - ing,

All is qui - et here be - low.

DIPPERS AND BEARS

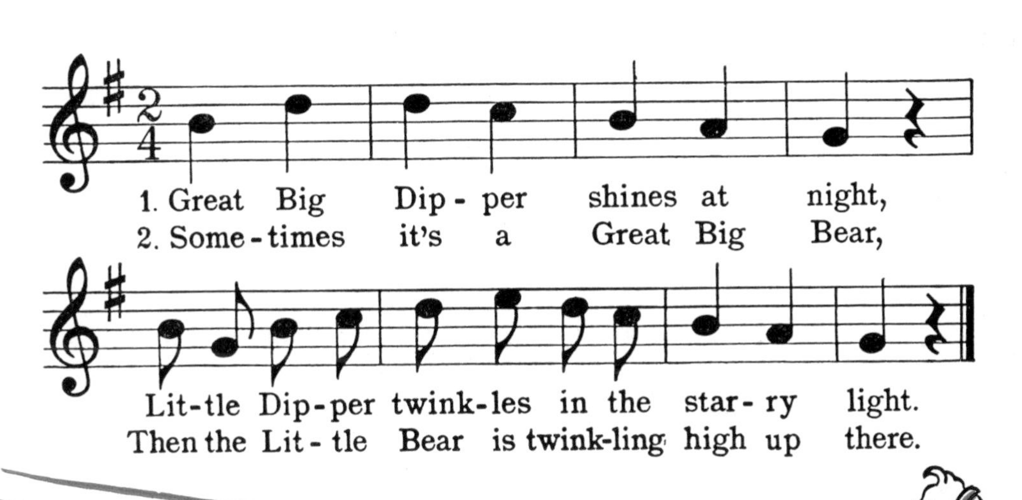
1. Great Big Dip - per shines at night,
2. Some - times it's a Great Big Bear,
Lit-tle Dip-per twink-les in the star - ry light.
Then the Lit - tle Bear is twink-ling high up there.

MAKING BELIEVE

THE LITTLE TURTLE

There was a lit-tle tur-tle, He lived in a box,
He swam in a pud-dle, He climbed on the rocks,
He snapped at a mos-qui-to, He snapped at a flea,
He snapped at a min-now, And he snapped at me.
Slower
He caught the mos-qui-to, He caught the flea,

T

Faster
He caught the min-now, But he did-n't catch me!

I WANT TO SAIL

Gaily
1. I want to sail in a bright blue boat,
2. I'll bring my doll and my ted - dy - bear,
With shin - ing sail - or but-tons on my coat,
Be - cause, of course, they need to take the air,
And o'er the wa - ter to light - ly float
We'll sail from here to the ev - 'ry - where
In sun - ny sum-mer weath - er.
And then come home to - geth - er.

THE TALE OF THE TAILLESS RABBIT

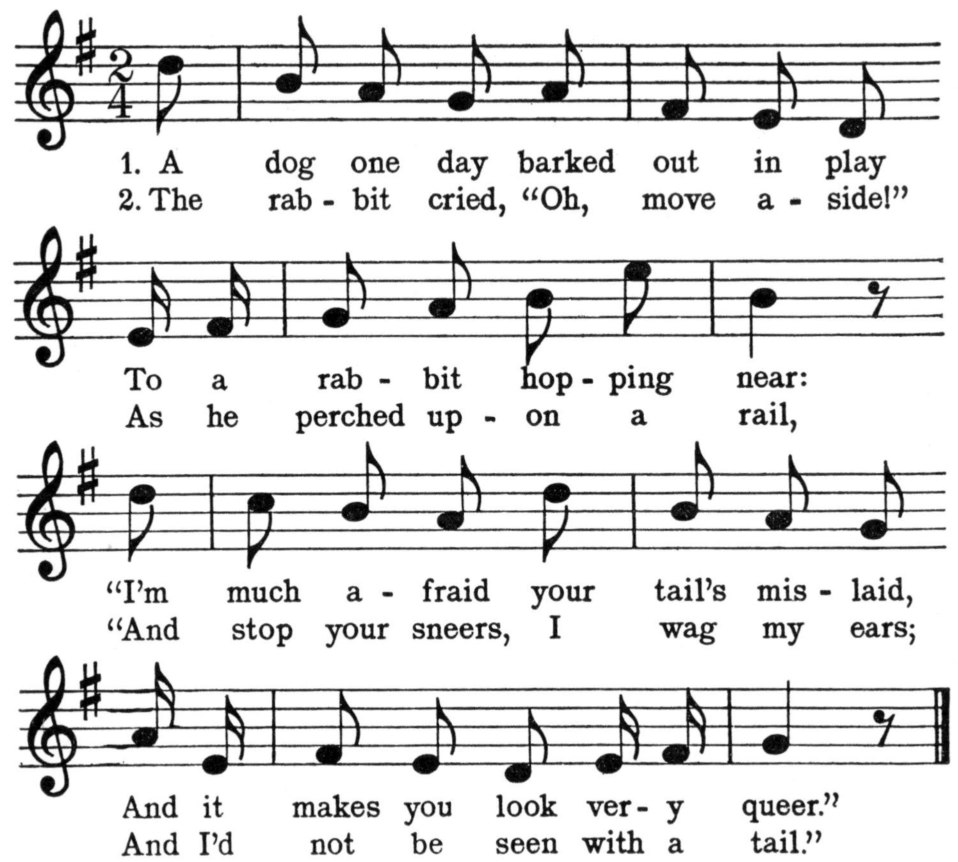
1. A dog one day barked out in play
2. The rab - bit cried, "Oh, move a - side!"
To a rab - bit hop - ping near:
As he perched up - on a rail,
"I'm much a - fraid your tail's mis - laid,
"And stop your sneers, I wag my ears;
And it makes you look ver - y queer."
And I'd not be seen with a tail."

THE MOON-CAKE

1. The moon is just a great big cake
2. I've of - ten watched it rise and rise–
3. And night by night it dis - ap-pears

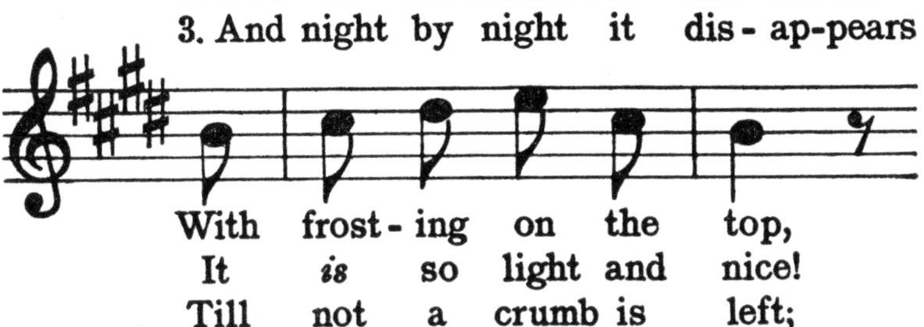

With frost - ing on the top,
It *is* so light and nice!
Till not a crumb is left;

Much larg - er than the kind you buy
But some-one comes and cuts that cake
I think per-haps the stars could tell

In an - y bak - er shop.
And steals it, slice by slice.
Who's guil - ty of the theft.

A descant for some of us to hum.

Hum____ Hum____

JAMES, THE BRAVE

Allegro
1. James J. Worth-ing-ton Brown,
2. James J. Worth-ing-ton Brown
He was a won-der-ful he-ro.
Thought for a min-ute, "Oh, dear, oh!"
He met with a snap-drag-on grouch-y and grim,
Then said to him-self, "I'll not trem-ble a bit,
He glow-ered at it and it glow-ered at him.
It's on-ly a flow'r and I'm big-ger than it."

James J. Worth - ing - ton Brown
James J. Worth - ing - ton Brown,
Felt his heart sink - ing to ze - ro.
He was a won - der - ful he - ro.

YOUNG PUSS

Young puss went a - walk-ing one bright sum-mer day;
She met a wee mous - ie who ran right a - way.
"Please stop, lit - tle mous - ie, and fro - lic with me."
"No, thank you," said mous-ie, "I'm late for my tea."
B

DONKEY MUSIC

1. Here is a tune that a don - key knows,
2. Where did he learn such a nois - y song?
This is the way that it al - ways goes,
Not ver - y good but it won't last long:
"Hee - haw, hee - haw, hee - haw!"
"Hee - haw, hee - haw, hee - haw!"

This tune was written by Wolfgang Mozart. It is very nice when hummed, or we may make our own words.

Hum
Hum
Hum
Hum

WHY?

Do you know why the shad-ows lie
Ver - y close when the sun is high?
Can you tell why they length-en so,
Ev - 'ry day when the sun is low?

THE CAT IN THE CHERRY TREE

1. One, two, three, come and see the
2. Is this the rea - son why: be -
cat in the cher - ry tree;
cause he likes cher - ry pie?
Nev - er a thing to do but
He shakes the full - est limb, but
sit there and look at you.
who'll make the pie for him?
Another descant.
Hum
Hum

THE GIANT COMES

1. Oh, moth - er dear, the gi - ant comes,
2. I hear his fierce fe - fi - fo - fums,
3. So moth - er bring a roast of beef,
4. Then moth - er bake a pie with plums,
5. And when he's had his fill to - day,
The gi - ant comes, I hear the drums!
Fe - fi - fo - fums, the gi - ant comes!
A roast of beef for his re - lief.
A pie with plums, the gi - ant comes!
His fill to - day, he'll go a - way.
Sing-ing re - fol - lol - de - li - do,
Sing-ing re - fol - lol - de - lay.

MARY'S LAMB

1. Oh, Ma - ry had a lit - tle lamb, And
2. He nev - er fol - lowed Ma - ry 'round, Tho'
3. She washed the lamb with Iv - 'ry soap To
4. So what could lit - tle Ma - ry do? The
fleece he did not lack, But
she was al - ways kind, He
make him white as snow, But
lamb was not to blame; Said
Moth - er Goose was quite up - set, Be -
would not go where Ma - ry went, But
when she'd washed him, he was still As
she: "Al - tho' he's black as ink, I
cause his fleece was black.
al - ways stayed be - hind.
black as an - y crow.
love him just the same."

THERE ONCE WAS A WREN

1. There once was a wren who lived up in a tree,
2. One day Mis-ter Rob-in came fly-ing that way,
3. There once was a bat and his col-or was brown;
4. And when it was morn-ing in Twick-en-ham town,

And all he could whis-tle was fid-dle-dee-dee;
And taught Mis-ter Wren to sing tra-la-la-lay;
He lived in a bel-fry in Twick-en-ham town;
This bat went to bed hang-ing all up-side-down;

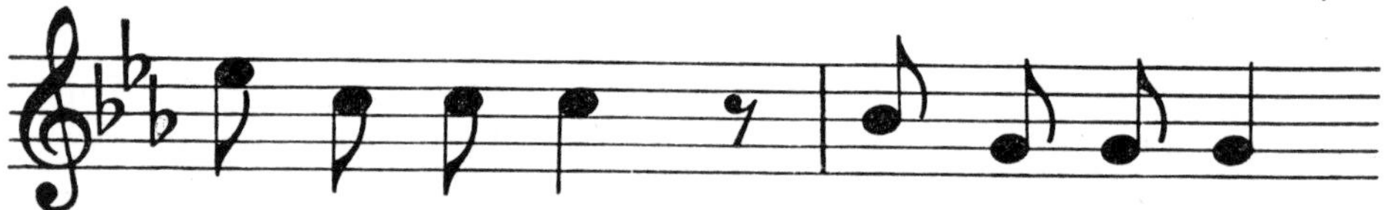

Fid-dle-dee-dee, fid-dle-dee-dee,
Tra-la-la-lay, tra-la-la-lay,
Twick-en-ham town, Twick-en-ham town,
All up-side-down, all up-side-down,

And all he could whis-tle was fid-dle-dee-dee.
He taught Mis-ter Wren to sing tra-la-la-lay.
He lived in a bel-fry in Twick-en-ham town.
This bat went to bed hang-ing all up-side-down.

The COBBLER and the ELVES

FIRST ELF
CURTAIN ELF
LEATHER MAN
PONY
RICH MAN
DANCING ELF
FOREST ELF
COBBLER'S WIFE
COBBLER

THE COBBLER AND THE ELVES

This play is adapted from a folk music play by Berta Elsmith. We can act it ourselves, or make a puppet show or a shadow play of it. We might even time it for a make-believe radio performance to be given in our schoolroom or auditorium. We can use a make-believe microphone, and have speeches for the announcer, just like a real radio performance.

Let us now go to the land of "Make-Believe", and watch the Cobbler and his good Wife work "make-believe" leather into "make-believe" shoes for "make-believe" people.

THE FOREST

(*The* FIRST ELF *comes through the curtain. Two* ELVES *creep around the edge of the curtain R. and L. and get ready to open the curtain.*)

FIRST ELF

People and friends, please listen to me;
A tale I will tell if it pleases you.
I can only tell half—ah! I am sorry—
But I must hurry back to act out my part.

(*The* ELVES *open the curtain. The stage is bare, save for four chairs.*)

(4)

(1)

(3) (2)

And now we see the Forest green,
The leafiest forest ever seen.

(*The* FOREST *enters up-stage and stands there.*)

Here dwelt a cobbler—this is he,
With his little wife for companee.

(COBBLER *and* WIFE *enter. Bow. He takes chair* (*1*); *she sits on the floor beside him.*)

See, there through the forest, the old, old road
That goes all the way to the Rich Man's abode.

(RICH MAN *enters and sits on chair* (2).)

Here is the field where ponies roam
Galloping, prancing around their wild home.

(*The* PONIES *gallop on to chair* (*4*).)

That house over there—look hard as you can—
You'll see is the home of the old leather man.

(LEATHER MAN *enters, bows and sits on chair* (3).)

Now, the cobbler could scarce keep the wolf from the door
For he and his wife were very poor.
But one night when they both were fast asleep
What *would* they have seen thro' the window peep?
Who would have guessed? Not they themselves!
Why, six little, wee little, green little elves.

(DANCING ELVES *tip-toe in; form a line and bow.*)

That last piece of leather lies right in their way
Where they tip-toe along on a silver moon ray.

(ELVES *tip-toe around and squat to left of the forest.*)

Now what happened next, on the stage you'll soon see,
And what happened later, if patient you'll be.
No more of the tale am I able to tell;
That it all happened once, you'll see very well.

(*The* ELF *bows, runs back and squats in front of the* FOREST. *The* CURTAIN ELVES *see that the curtain hangs straight, then sit cross-legged, one on each side of the stage, watching the action and singing the choruses.*)

(COBBLER *gets ready to work.* ELVES *scatter a bit.*)

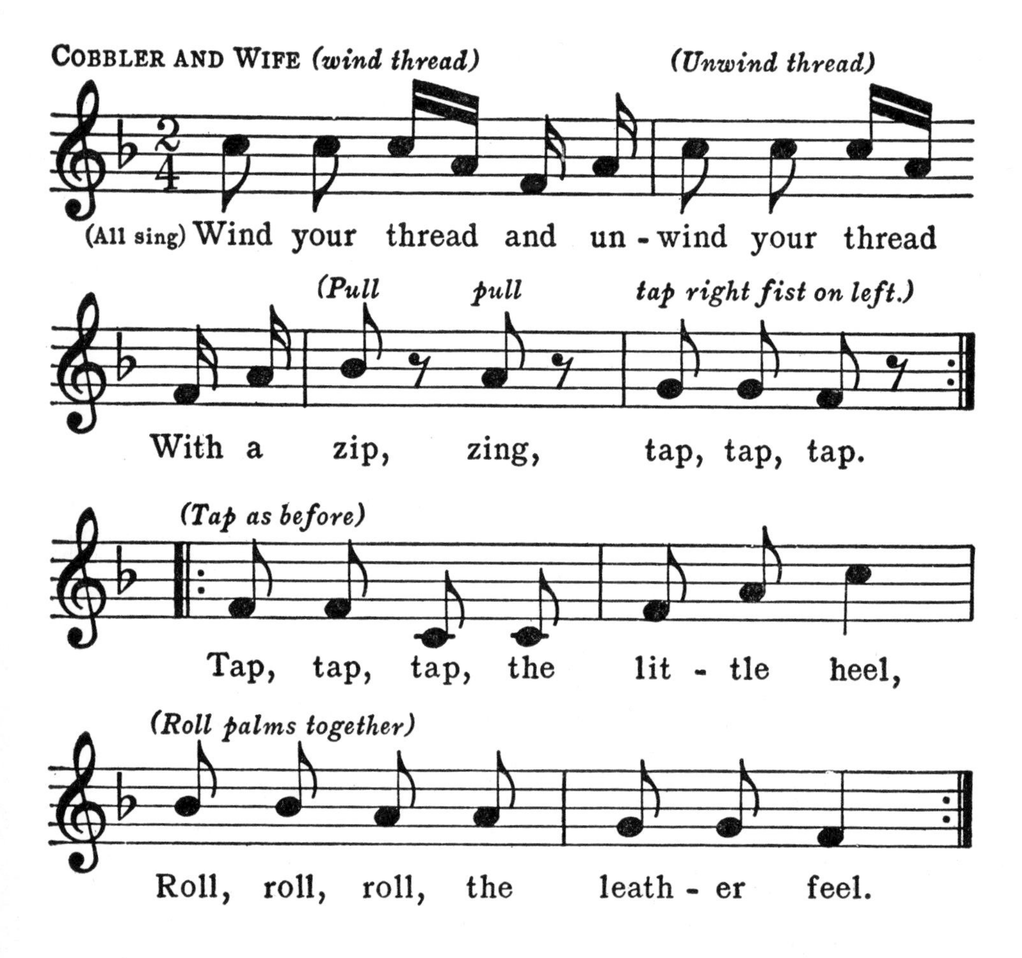

COBBLER AND WIFE (wind thread)
(Unwind thread)
(All sing) Wind your thread and un - wind your thread
(Pull pull tap right fist on left.)
With a zip, zing, tap, tap, tap.
(Tap as before)
Tap, tap, tap, the lit - tle heel,
(Roll palms together)
Roll, roll, roll, the leath - er feel.

(*They stop work, having no more leather.*)

COBBLER	Oh dear! I'm so tired.
WIFE	It's bed-time, dear. Put away your work.
COBBLER	Work! There's no work to do.
	My last leather—and no customer—
WIFE	Come! Maybe a surprise will happen.
COBBLER	Do you think leather will happen?
WIFE	Who can tell? Put the shoes here.
COBBLER	I'll see what I can do tomorrow.
WIFE	Bed-time now, though.

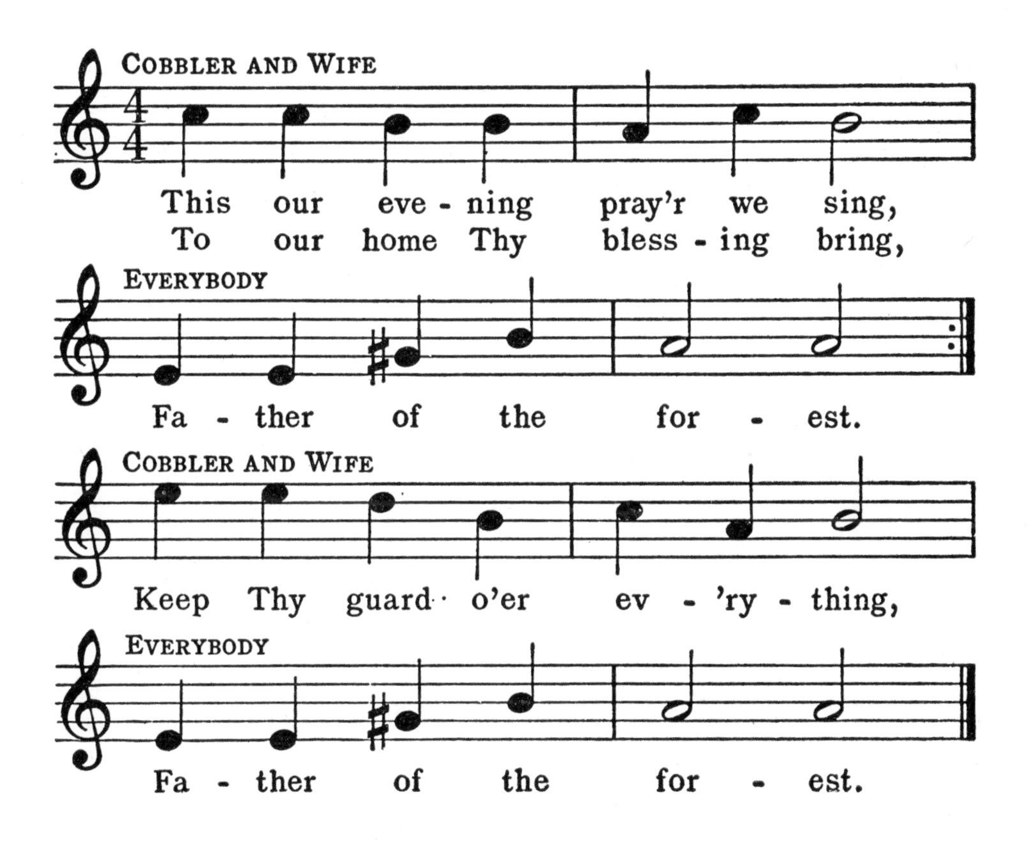
COBBLER AND WIFE
This our eve - ning pray'r we sing,
To our home Thy bless - ing bring,
EVERYBODY
Fa - ther of the for - est.
COBBLER AND WIFE
Keep Thy guard o'er ev - 'ry - thing,
EVERYBODY
Fa - ther of the for - est.

(They curl up at front of stage and go to sleep.)

(ELVES *dance round chair (1).*)

(All) Tra la la la la la, la, Tra la la la la
Tip - toe, tip - toe, squat, Tip - toe, tip - toe,
(What was that?)
la, la, Tra la la la la la la la
squat, Tip - toe, tip - toe, jump and turn,
Tra la la la la la la la la la.
Run - - - - - - - - - - - - - - - - - - - and squat.- - -

(*End sitting cross-legged around center chair (1).*)

(ELVES *go through the motions of making shoes, humming the first song, then dance again, lay the make-believe shoes on the chair, and go to their places. The* COBBLER *and his* WIFE *wake up.*)

COBBLER I dreamed I heard singing.

WIFE No, no. It was little feet dancing.

COBBLER Oh dear! I had forgotten.
There's no leather and no money.

WIFE But there's bread and tea. Let's eat!

(*They find the shoes.*)

Cobbler and Wife 1. O look! O look! I can't be - lieve my eyes! This love - ly pair of per - fect shoes, My dear! what a sur - prise!
2. A heel of red! A tas - sel at the top! O say at once you nev - er saw Such gay shoes in a shop!
(All) 3. O joy! O bliss! They can't be - lieve their eyes! How cle - ver and how right of us To give them this sur - prise!

(ELVES *dance as all sing the 3rd verse.*)

(*The* RICH MAN, *holding a big bag of gold comes to chair* (1) *and knocks. The* COBBLER *and his* WIFE *jump.* WIFE *opens door and all bow.*)

COBBLER *and* WIFE *on "tra-la"*,

1. *Bow to* RICH MAN.
2. *Show shoes to* RICH MAN.
3. *Clap hands and jump for joy.*

(Rich Man) I want a pair of shoes, tra - la,
(Cob. and Wife) O see this love - ly pair, tra - la,
(Rich Man) They seem to suit me quite, tra - la,
I need a pair of shoes, tra - la,
Of shoes so ver - y fair, tra - la,
They're not a bit too tight, tra - la.
To walk in or to hop,
We prom - ise they will hop,
I like them gay and bright,
With a tas - sel at the top.
With a tas - sel at the top.
So they're just ex - act - ly right.

1. COBBLER *and* WIFE *look at* RICH MAN.

2. RICH MAN *looks at shoes.*

3. *All three join hands and dance.*

ALL
O fa - la - la, lo, O fa - la - la, lo,
Some shoes in which to hop.
Pray try them while you stop.
They seem to suit him quite.
O fa - la - la, lo, O fa - la - la, lo,
With tas - sels at the top.
The tas - sel's at the top.
In fact they are just right.

(*After verse 2,* RICH MAN *sits on chair (1), tries on shoes, stamps feet, walks about and looks pleased. Sings verse 3.*)

RICH MAN — May I leave this gold for the shoes?

COBBLER — Thank you, sir.

RICH MAN — I like the shoes. Pray visit me with your wife when you pass by.

COBBLER — Thank you, sir. It's kind of you, sir.

RICH MAN — I shall send my friends to you. Good-day

COBBLER — Good-day. Thank you, sir.

(RICH MAN *returns to his chair.* COBBLER *and* WIFE *sing.*)

I dreamed it all last night, tra-la,
They weren't a bit too tight, tra-la,
I wished with all my might
That the shoes would be just right.

ALL (*singing*) — O fa-la-la-lo, O fa-la-la-lo,
They wished with all their might.
O fa-la-la-lo, O fa-la-la-lo,
In this they did just right.

WIFE — What shall we do with this bag of gold?

COBBLER — Let us gallop to the Leather Man.
We will buy all his beautiful leather.

WIFE — Yes, but where did the shoes come from?
How did it all happen?

COBBLER — We can find out. I'll tell you later.
Let's hurry and get our leather first.

WIFE — Good. I'll put on my bonnet right now.

(COBBLER *and* WIFE *each catch two ponies, and all gallop around the stage as they sing.*)

Lively
Come, my po-nies and gal - lop, And
Mas - ter Leath-er - man, hear ye, Oh,
gal - lop, and gal - lop; Come, my po-nies and
hear ye, oh, hear ye, Mas - ter Leath-er - man,
Fine
gal - lop, Now whoa! whoa! whoa!
hear ye, We're on our way!
(stop by RICH MAN who rises)
Sir, we stop up - on our way To greet you on this
(Turn ponies around) Da Capo
sun - ny day, Then off we go - o!

(*They stop by the* Leather Man.)

Leather Man Good-day, Master and Mistress Shoemaker.
'Tis a long time since you were here.

Cobbler Ah, but to-day we come with good fortune.
Look at this heavy bag of gold!
We will buy leather.

Leather Man Oh, what a lot of gold!
You will want my very best skins.

All Three (*talking at once*) Will this color wear well?
I like this pink one.
This really is the very best.

(*They look at the make-believe leather in his store. He fills their arms with it.*)

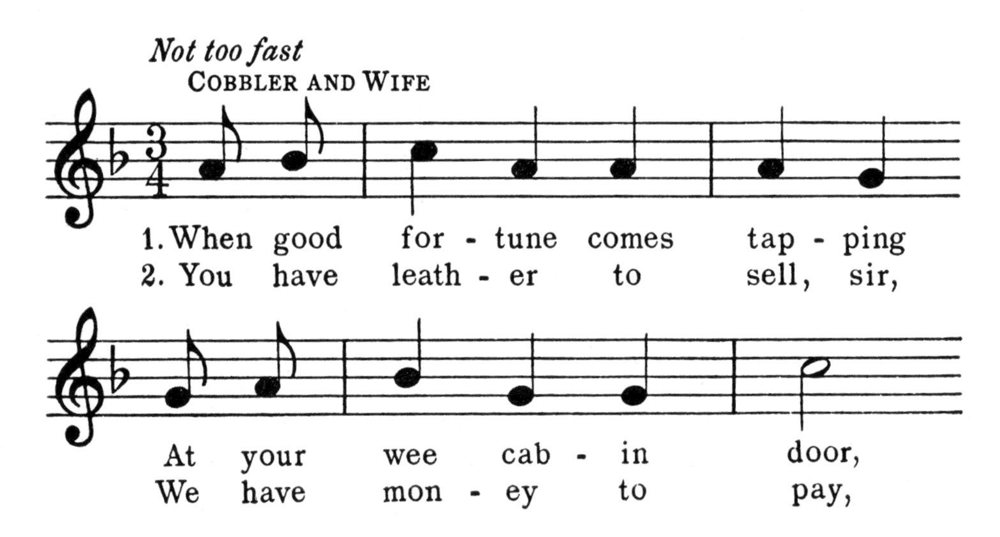
Not too fast
COBBLER AND WIFE
1. When good for - tune comes tap - ping
2. You have leath - er to sell, sir,
At your wee cab - in door,
We have mon - ey to pay,

GOLD
GOLD

If she catch - es you nap - ping,
So it's all ver - y well, sir,
She will come there no more.
And we bid you good - day.

(COBBLER, WIFE *and* PONIES *gallop to their chairs singing the first part of "Come, My Ponies".*)

COBBLER We'll cut up this leather before we go to bed, but we won't finish any shoes.

WIFE Oh let's finish some shoes. You know the Rich Man said he'd send his friends.

COBBLER Yes, I know, but don't you want to find out who helped us last night?

WIFE To be sure. How can we do it?

COBBLER We'll leave the unfinished shoes and go to bed, but we'll only pretend to sleep. Then whoever finished the shoes last night may come again to see if there is more work to be done.

WIFE Oh yes! And we'll stay awake and see them. O, let's hurry and get ready!

(COBBLER *and* WIFE *sing and act out "Wind Your Thread". Then they put down the leather and sing, to the tune of the Prayer.*)

C & W	In the woodland shadows deep,
ALL	Father of the forest
C & W	Save the tiny ones that creep,
ALL	Father of the forest
C & W	As they softly go to sleep
ALL	Father of the forest.

(*They go to sleep on the floor.* ELVES *tip-toe in, hum, dance and work as before.* COBBLER *and* WIFE *peek at them.* ELVES *repeat their dance, put the work on chair (1) and squat at left of* FOREST.)

(COBBLER *and* WIFE *wake up and rush to chair at center.*)

WIFE	Oh, the darling things. But won't they be cold in winter just dressed in autumn leaves?
COBBLER	I will make them some tiny, furry shoes.
WIFE	And I will make them some nice, woolly coats.

(*They sit down and work, singing this song.*)

(On each verse an elfin tip-toes forward and peeks.)
Once up - on a time there was a
Ev - 'ry day at sun - set he came
By and by the win - try winds be -
ti - ny elf Hid him - self
danc - ing out, Round a - bout,
gan to blow, And the snow
(Runs back to place)
Un - der - neath a mush - room
Call - ing oth - er elves to
Chased the lit - tle elf in -
where he kept his pelf.
play, I have no doubt.
to his cave be - low.

(COBBLER *and* WIFE *place the make-believe clothes on the chair (1) and sing, to the tune of the Prayer.*)

C & W	Silver shadows fall tonight,
ALL	Father of the forest,
C & W	In the shadow of Thy might,
ALL	Father of the forest.
C & W	Keep us, child and elf and sprite,
ALL	Father of the forest.

(COBBLER *and* WIFE *go to bed as before, but peek, then sit up and watch as the* ELVES *hum and dance to the dance music and find the clothes. The* CURTAIN *is closed quickly by the* CURTAIN ELVES. *The* FIRST ELF *sticks his head through the curtain and says*)

The story goes on that from that day to this
They weren't seen again,—but they left you this kiss.

(*He throws a kiss to the audience and vanishes.*)

THE PLAY ENDS

SING WITH ME!

Chil- dren, play- mates, come and sing,
Hearts are hap - py, voic - es ring.
Light - ly, sweet - ly, sing with me,
Light - ly, sweet - ly, sing with me.
Chil - dren, play- mates, come and sing,
Hearts are hap - py, voic - es ring.

This tune is sung by French boys and girls, and in America we often sing it to "Twinkle, twinkle, little star." Here you will find new words.

In these little short songs, can you find parts of the music and words of "Sing with me!"?

Sing with me, sing with me.
Hearts are hap - py, voic - es ring.
Light - ly, sweet - ly, sing with me.
Hearts are hap - py, voic - es ring.
o-o-o-o-o-o-o-o-o-o-o-o-

Chil- dren, chil- dren, come and sing.
Chil - dren, chil- dren, voic - es ring.
Come and sing, come and sing.
Hearts are hap - py, voic - es ring.
Chil- dren, play-mates, sing with me,
Come and sing, voic - es ring.
Do you see how the songs always end?
Why is this a good ending for a song?

GOOD COWS

1. Gen - tle cows are slow - ly go - ing,
2. Now the milk is in the dai - ry,
Out where the mead - ow grass is grow - ing.
Qui - et and cool and clean and air - y,
Then at night you will hear them low - ing.
Milk for Su - san and Dick and Ma - ry,
Milk - ing time has come, you see.
Good fresh milk for you and me.

Do you find any phrases that are alike in this song?
Are there any phrases that are almost alike?

STRANGE SHOES

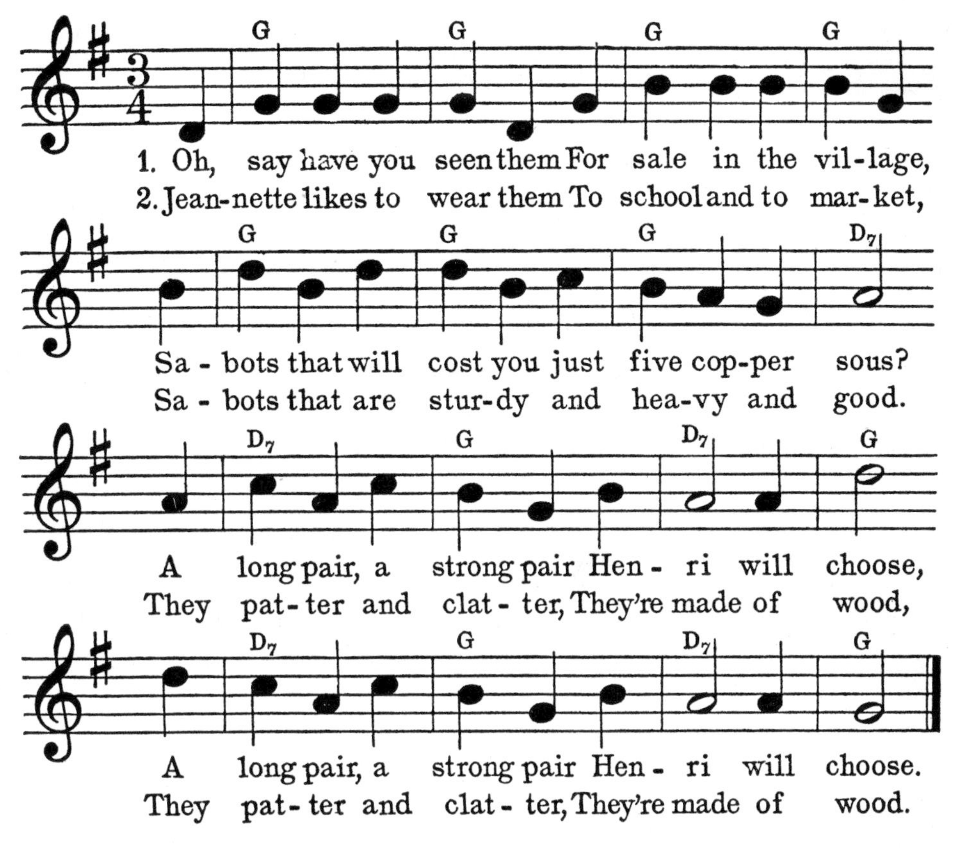
1. Oh, say have you seen them For sale in the vil-lage,
2. Jean-nette likes to wear them To school and to mar-ket,
Sa - bots that will cost you just five cop-per sous?
Sa - bots that are stur-dy and hea-vy and good.
A long pair, a strong pair Hen - ri will choose,
They pat - ter and clat - ter, They're made of wood,
A long pair, a strong pair Hen - ri will choose.
They pat - ter and clat - ter, They're made of wood.

"Sabots" are wooden shoes. The word is pronounced sä-bōs.

For this song you need play only two chords on the autoharp, and they will sound well with your singing.

FOR CHRISTMAS

MAKING CHRISTMAS PRESENTS

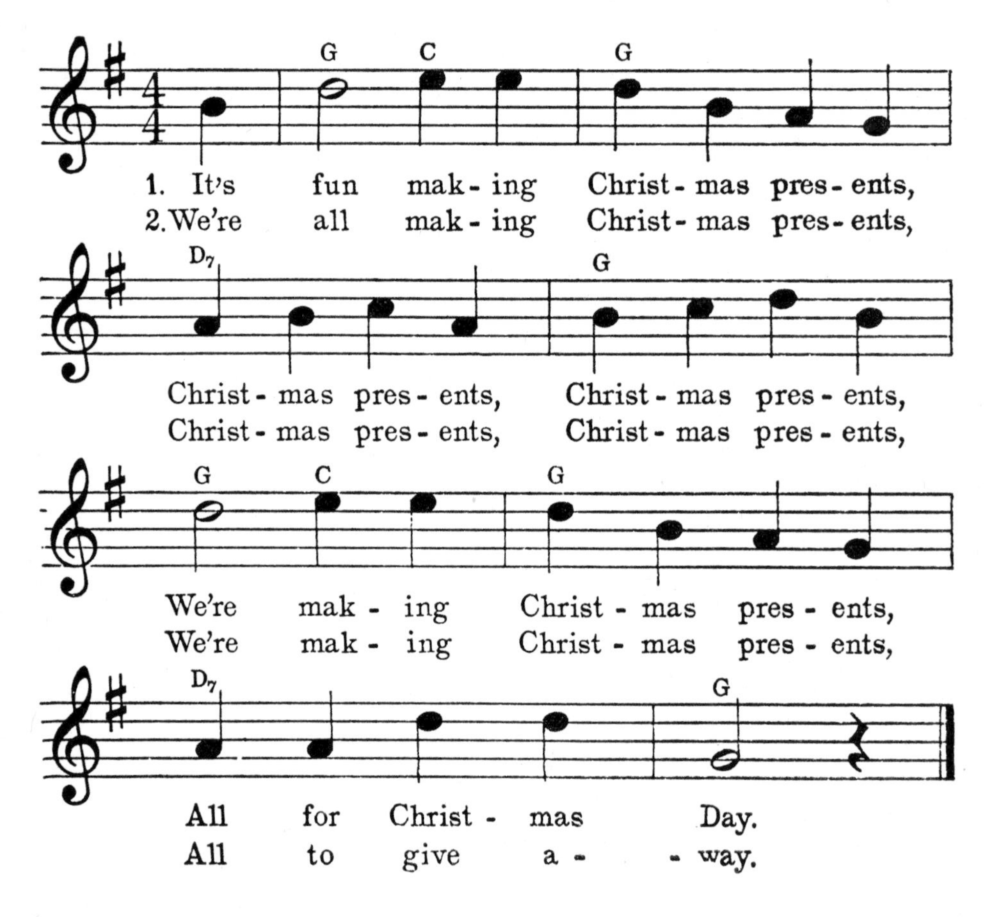
G C G
1. It's fun mak - ing Christ - mas pres - ents,
2. We're all mak - ing Christ - mas pres - ents,
D7 G
Christ - mas pres - ents, Christ - mas pres - ents,
Christ - mas pres - ents, Christ - mas pres - ents,
G C G
We're mak - ing Christ - mas pres - ents,
We're mak - ing Christ - mas pres - ents,
D7 G
All for Christ - mas Day.
All to give a - - way.

This song will need three chords on the autoharp.

CHRISTMAS SNOW

1. In - side the Christ - mas tree is bright,
2. The chil - dren go to co - sy beds,
Its lights are all a - glow.
And as they go they say,
Out - doors come drift - ing through the night
"To - mor - row we can take our sleds,
The ti - ny flakes of snow.
And coast on Christ - mas Day."
Here is a little tune without any words. Can you write some words about Christmas that will fit the music? Then name the song.

AROUND THE CHRISTMAS TREE

1. Christ-mas a - gain, It's Christ-mas a - gain!
2. Do come and see The gay Christ-mas tree.
We're hap - py, so we dance and ca - per,
With strings of twink-ling lights we wound it.
Glad when we see The bright Christ-mas tree,
Now for some fun, Come on, ev - 'ry one,
With gifts wrapped in col- ored pa - per.
We'll join hands and dance a - round it.

Why not make up your own dance around the tree?

Can you make a Christmas tune for this little verse?

MY CHRISTMAS STOCKING

I hang my stocking on Christmas Eve.
It's thin, when I go to bed,
But in the morning, would you believe,
It's fat as can be, instead!

BREAK THE PIÑATA

F F B♭ F
1. "Break the piñ - a - ta!" chil-dren are cry-ing,
2. Now come and gath-er sweets that it boast-ed,
3. Pine-ap-ples, can-died, ap-ples to treas-ure,
F C7 C7 F
"Find it and break it, and send sweet-meats fly-ing!"
Pea-nuts and chest-nuts and al-monds well roast-ed.
All of our guests have a share in our pleas-ure.

At Christmas time in Mexico there hangs from the ceiling a clay bowl called a *piñata,* which is filled with candy and nuts. One child is blindfolded, turned around several times, and then given a stick with which to break the piñata. Everyone has fun watching him try to find it. When the piñata is finally broken, the children scramble for the goodies.

SWINGING IN THE LANE

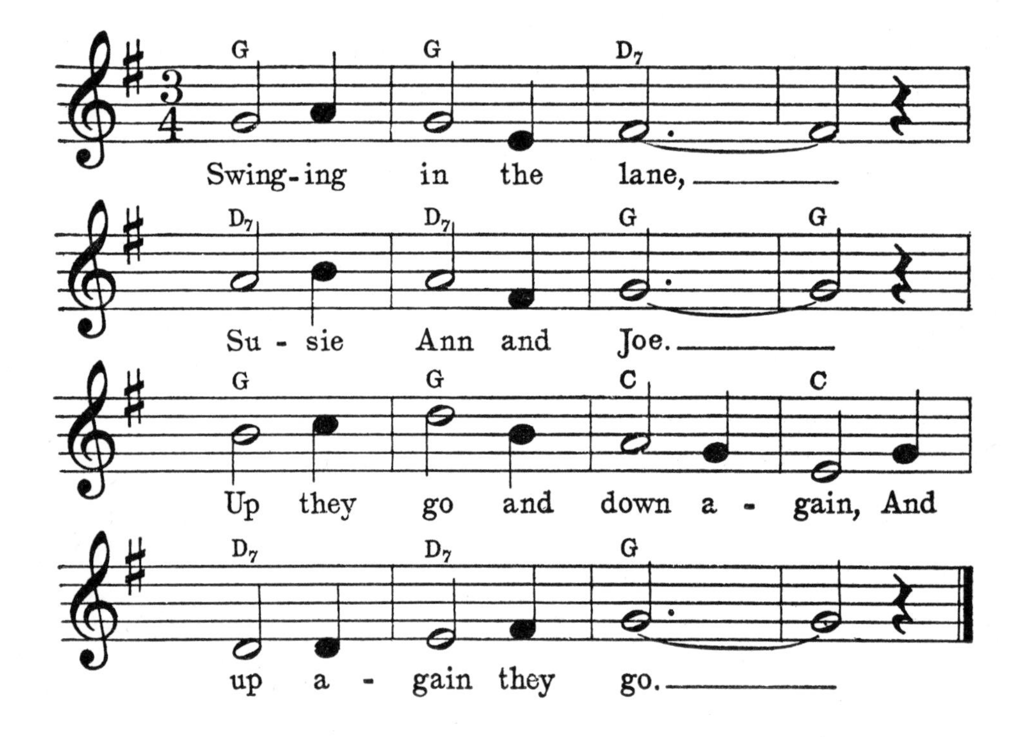
G G D7
Swing-ing in the lane,
D7 D7 G G
Su - sie Ann and Joe.
G G C C
Up they go and down a - gain, And
D7 D7 G
up a - gain they go.

Double circle of couples facing. Each couple joins crossed hands to make a "swing." At each swing a third child stands, facing clockwise. This child puts his hands on the swing, and balances forward and back, pushing the swing up and letting it come back again. Use one measure for each motion. On the word "go" he runs under his swing, pushing it up, and goes on to the next swing. Repeat. Each player should have a turn at pushing the swing.

JUMP JIM CROW

Jump, jump, and jump Jim Crow,
Jump jump jump jump jump
Take a lit- tle twirl and then a - way we go.
Turn partner in 7 running steps
Slide, slide and stamp just so, Then you
Slide right to meet new partner stamp stamp stamp
take an- oth- er part-ner and you jump Jim Crow.
Turn new partner in 4 steps jump jump jump

Can you make up your own tune for these
words, and then sing the song and act it out?

PINTO AND I

Jog, jog along, my pinto pal,
Jog, jog along from the old corral.
Jog, jog along, jog on, I say.
We must ride the range today.

JOHN, THE MILLER

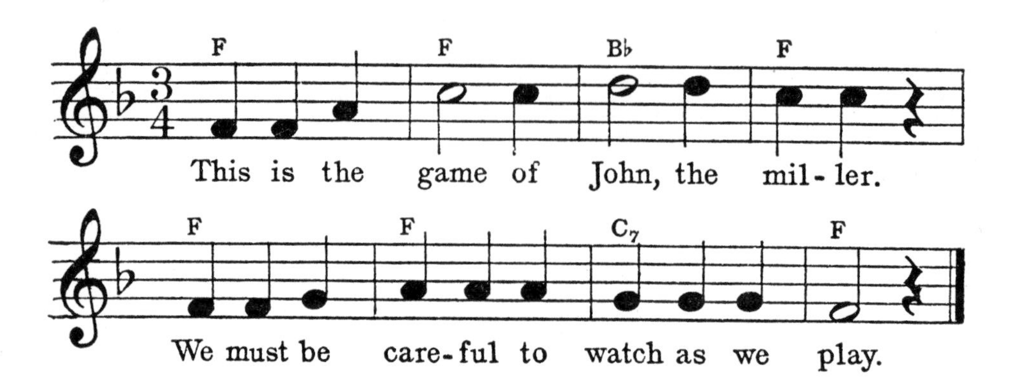
F F B♭ F
This is the game of John, the mil- ler.
F F C7 F
We must be care- ful to watch as we play.

All sit on the floor in a circle but John, who stands in the center and gives each one something to act out, such as sawing wood, washing clothes, or playing the fiddle.

All sing the song, while John makes believe to turn the mill wheel just as the music tells him to turn it. Then all sing the song over and over, while John keeps turning the wheel, and each one acts out his part in time to the music.

When John is ready, he changes from turning the wheel to something that another child is doing (such as sawing wood). Then that one must quickly change to turning the wheel. If he does not change, and John catches him, John tells him to do something silly, like hopping on one foot. Then the game starts all over again. Better watch out!

WHAT DO THEY DO?

1. Oh, see the bus-y tai - lor, What does he do?
2. Oh, see the bus-y cob-bler, What does he do?
3. Oh, see the bus-y bak- er, What does he do?
4. Oh, see the bus-y farm-er, What does he do?
5. Oh, see the bus-y cow- boy, What does he do?
What does he do? A - snip-snip-snip his
What does he do? He cuts a sole of
What does he do? He stirs a spic - y
What does he do? At first he plows and
What does he do? A - cross the range he's
shears are go - ing, Then he sits there sew- ing, sew-ing.
good stout leath-er, Nails the sole and shoe to - geth- er.
cake he's mak-ing, Cuts out cook - ies, starts them bak-ing.
then he's sow-ing, When the weeds come, then he's hoe-ing.
rid- ing, rid- ing, While the graz - ing herd he's guid-ing.

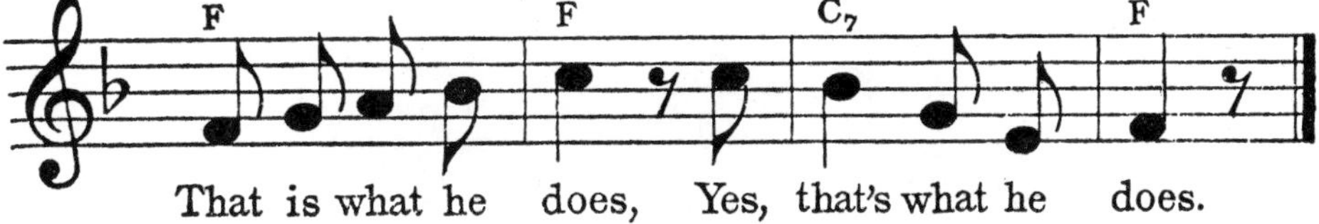
That is what he does, Yes, that's what he does.

Can you act out all the things these workers do?

PENNY, PENNY

G G
Pen - ny, pen - ny, How you wan - der,
G D7 G
From the one hand to the oth - er.
G C D7 G
Is it fair, Is it fair,
G D7 G D7 G
To leave poor Ma - ry stand - ing there?
(any name)

The players stand in a circle, with one child in the center. As they sing, they pass a penny around the circle, from one to another, pretending to pass it even when they do not have it. The center player tries to guess who has the penny. If his guess is right, the child who had the penny goes to the center, and the game begins again.

GOING TO BOSTON

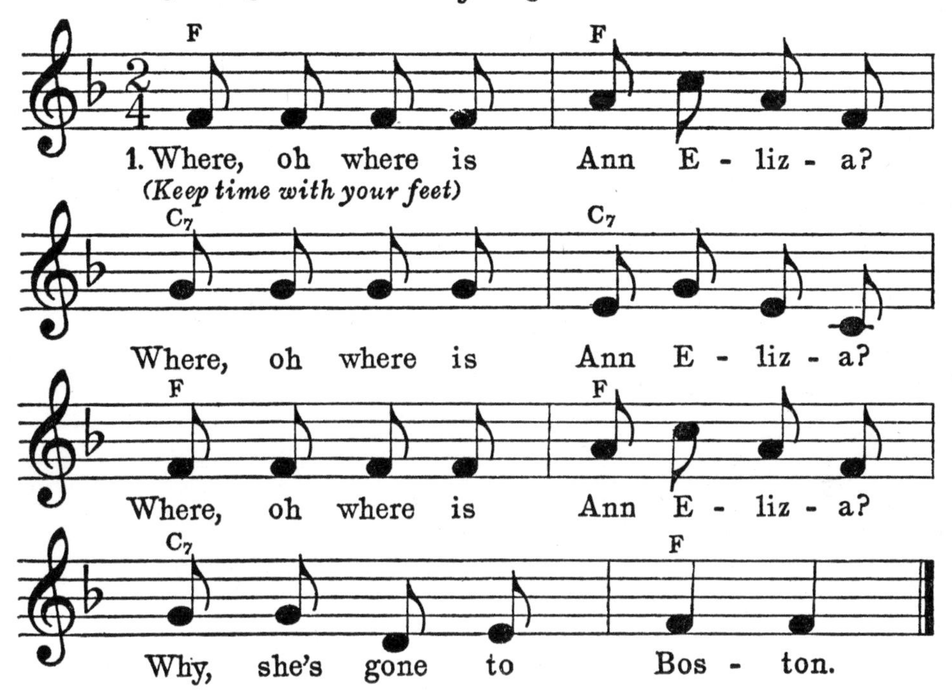

Boys and girls stand in two facing lines.
F
F
1. Where, oh where is Ann E - liz - a?
(Keep time with your feet)
C7
C7
Where, oh where is Ann E - liz - a?
F
F
Where, oh where is Ann E - liz - a?
C7
F
Why, she's gone to Bos - ton.

2. Come along, girls, we'll go to Boston, *(3 times)*
   Early in the morning.
   (Girls march around the line of boys and back to place.)

3. Where, oh, where is Henry Allen? *(3 times)*
   Why, he's gone to Boston.
   (Keep time with your feet.)

4. Saddle up, boys, we'll go to Boston, *(3 times)*
   Early in the morning.
   (Boys gallop around line of girls and back to place.)

5. Come along, folks, we'll go to Boston, *(3 times)*
   Early in the morning.
   (Each boy takes hands of girl across from him, and all slide 8 steps to the side and back to place.)

CLASSIFIED INDEX

HOME AND FAMILY
See general section "At Home", pages 5–29. Additional songs are:
Busy Clock, A, 136
Little Black Cat, 126
Mince Pie, 87
Mother's Day, 101
My Daddy's Watch, 137
My Present, 50
Slumber Song, A, 131
When the Postman Comes, 43

SINGING WITH THE GROWN-UPS
America, 23
Billy Magee Magaw, 26
Jingle Bells, 111
Nelly Bly, 24
Silent Night, 25
Yankee Doodle, 94

PETS, TOYS, AND GAMES
See general section "At Home", pages 5–29.
Chinese New Year, 128
Jolly Tar, A, 71
Little Black Cat, 126
See-saw, 130
Wonderful Man of Snow, A, 92
Young Puss, 146

FOOD AND CLOTHING
Ant Reporter Interviews the Bees, The, 72
Cobbler, The, 46
Cookies, 12
Copying Mother, 9
Grocer Man, The, 52
Hot Gingerbread, 13
I want a Pair of Shoes, 162
Mince Pie, 87
My Present, 50
My Shopping List, 51
New Shoes, 62
New Simple Simon, 135
O Look! O Look! 161
Our Christmas Pie, 90
Shoes, 47
Song of the Corn, 79
They're Useful, 62
When Mother Sews, 8

SCHOOL
Good Morning, We Say, 127
June, 102
Musical Mix-Up, A, 120
Our School Bus, 67
Thanksgiving, 127
We Give Thanks, 88
Yoo-Hoo, 119

COMMUNITY LIFE
See general section "Shopping", pages 42–52. Additional songs are:
Hurdy-Gurdy Man, The, 100
Hy-Ya-Ho, 78
Our School Bus, 67
What I Like, 17

SOCIAL RELATIONSHIPS
Ant Reporter Interviews the Bees, The, 72
Cobbler, The, 46
Good Morning, We Say, 127
He Whistled Just the Same, 21
I Walk and Talk with Father, 10
Mother's Day, 101
My Present, 50
My Shopping List, 51
New Simple Simon, 135
Policeman, The, 44
Shopping, 42
Smoking the Peace Pipe, 80
Such a Difference, 28
Two Valentines, 93
We Give Thanks, 88
When Good Fortune Comes Tapping, 166
When the Postman Comes, 43
Yoo-Hoo, 119

CHARACTER
Ant Reporter Interviews the Bees, The, 72
Come, Little Chipmunk, 32
Fireman, The, 49
Gray Squirrel, 84
He Whistled Just the Same, 21
Hy-Ya-Ho, 78
In Fourteen Hundred, Ninety-Two, 83
Mother's Day, 101
My Morning Song, 5
Such a Difference, 28
We Give Thanks, 88
When Good Fortune Comes Tapping, 166

CIRCUS AND ZOO
See general section "Going to the Circus", pages 54–58

WAYS TO TRAVEL
Come, My Ponies, 165
Daily Express, The, 68
I Want to Sail, 141
Jolly Tar, A, 71
Liner and the Tug, The, 70
Our School Bus, 67
Three Blind Mice, 66
Trim, Trig Trailer, The, 64
Trot, Trot, Trot, 20
Streamline Trains, 129

HEALTH AND SAFETY
Daily Express, The, 68
Fireman, The, 49
Grocer Man, The, 52
He Whistled Just the Same, 21
New Shoes, 62
Policeman, The, 44
Such a Difference, 28
Swish!, 50
They're Useful, 62
Three Blind Mice, 66

DEVOTION
America, 23
Easter Time, 99
Evening Prayer, 159, 168, 170
Silent Night, 25
Thanksgiving, 127
We Give Thanks, 88

PATRIOTIC SONGS
America, 23
When Bands Began to Play, 103
Yankee Doodle, 94

NATURE
All in the Tree, 39
Ant Reporter Interviews the Bees, The, 72
Big, Big Sky, The, 121
Buttercups, Too, 101
Dippers and Bears, 139
Duet, A, 113
Easter Time, 99
Good Morning, 6
Growing, 96
Hello! 35
Moon-Cake, The, 143
Orange Moon, 41
Sing a Song of Seasons, 82
Song of the Corn, 79
Star, 123
Sun and Moon, 122
Waves and I, The, 104
Why? 148

ANIMALS
Big, Brown Bear, 57
Billy Magee Magaw, 26
Come, Little Chipmunk, 32
Donkey Music, 147
Funny Bunny, 37
Gray Squirrel, 84
Hop, Little Frog, 40
Lambkin, The, 38
Little Black Cat, 126
Little Bunny Hops, 31
Little Turtle, The, 140
Moving Day, 37
Ragtag and Bobtail, 16
See That Elephant, 58
Tale of the Tailless Rabbit, The, 142
Trot, Trot, Trot, 20
What I Like, 17
Young Puss, 146

BIRDS AND BUGS
Ant Reporter Interviews the Bees, The, 72
Butterflies, 33
Foreign Language, A, 102
Geese, 36
Guess Who I Am, 30
Lightning Bug, 131
Little Brown Bug, 33
Miss Chickadee, 96
Noisy Bird, A, 36
Summer Lullaby, 105
There Once Was a Wren, 152
Wish, A, 34
Woodpecker, The, 117

WIND AND WEATHER
How They Grow, 134
Little Wind, 61
March Wind, 97
New Shoes, 62
Rainbow, 125
Rain or Shine, 60
Storm Clouds, 124
They're Useful, 62
Waves, 138
Weather Vane, 59
Who Has Seen the Wind? 63

FARM LIFE
Ant Reporter Interviews the Bees, The, 72
Billy Magee Magaw, 26
Geese, 36
Growing, 96
How They Grow, 134
Lambkin, The, 38
Song of the Corn, 79
So-Sow-Sewing, 109

SEASONS
For Autumn, Winter, Spring and Summer songs, in the order named, see the general section "Around the Calendar", pages 82–105. Additional Songs are:

Autumn
Come, Little Chipmunk, 32
Winter
Jingle Bells, 111
Once Upon a Time, 169
Spring
Billy Magee Magaw, 26
Little Wind, 61
Summer
Guess Who I Am, 30
How They Grow, 134
I Want to Sail, 141
Lightning Bug, 131
Rainbow, 125
Storm Clouds, 124

SPECIAL DAYS

See general section "Around the Calendar", 82–105; For Christmas, 176–179. Additional songs are:
America, 23
Band Music, 132
Silent Night, 25
Stately Dance, A, 106
Thanksgiving, 127

MORNING AND EVENING

Baby, Sleep, 128
Bugle, Blow, 134
Cradle Song, 29
Dippers and Bears, 139
Evening Prayer, 159
Good Morning, 6
Good Morning, We Say, 127
Lullaby, 81
Music on the Air, 22
My Morning Song, 5
Sleepy Song, 129
Slumber Song, 131
Such a Difference, 28
Summer Lullaby, 105
Sunrise Song, 77
Twilight, 126

MASTER COMPOSERS

Busy Clock, A (Jensen), 136
Foreign Language, A (Reinecke), 102
Jolly Miller, The (Schubert), 53
Minuet (Mozart), 95
Moment Musicale (Schubert), 160
Mother's Day (von Flotow), 101
Spring Greeting (Mendelssohn), 100
Stately Dance, A (Grieg), 106
Thanksgiving (Bach), 127
Theme (Mozart), 147

ADVENTURE

All in the Tree, 39
Down and Back, 91
In Fourteen Hundred Ninety-Two, 83
I Walk and Talk with Father, 10
I Want to Sail, 141
James, the Brave, 144
Jolly Miller, The, 53
Jolly Tar, A, 71
Occupations, 15
Streamline Trains, 129
Trim, Trig Trailer, The, 64
Wandering, 132

FANCY AND MAKE BELIEVE

See general section "Making Believe", pages 140–152. Additional songs are:
Ant Reporter Interviews the Bees, The, 72
Daily Express, The, 68
Foreign Language, A, 102
Hello! 35
In a Hickory Nut, 86
Miss Chickadee, 96
Occupations, 15
Once upon a Time, 169

FUN AND NONSENSE

See general section "Making Believe", pages 140–152. Additional songs are:
Billy Magee Magaw, 26
Clown, The, 55
Down and Back, 91
Gay Little Dance, A, 108
Guess Who I Am, 30
Hippity Hop, 112
Long Trip, A, 133
Moving Day, 37
Musical Mix-Up, A, 120
New Simple Simon, 135

ACTING, DANCING AND GAME SONGS

See general sections "We Sing, Play and Dance", pages 106–116; "An Indian's Day", pages 77–81; "The Ant Reporter Interviews the Bees", pages 72–76; "The Cobbler and the Elves", 153–170; Singing Games, 180–185. Additional songs are:
Band Music, 132
Big Brown Bear, 57
Copying Mother, 9
High, Low, 130
Hobby Horse, 19
Minuet, 95
Seesaw, 130
When Bands Begin to Play, 103
Wish, A, 34

RHYTHM BAND

See "We Sing, Play and Dance", pages 106–116.

INDIAN SONGS

See "An Indian's Day", pages 77–81.

CREATIVE EXPRESSION

Tuneful Tim's Letter, 117
Words for original tunes, 42–61–63–65–69–71–110–118
Tunes for original words, 95–147

VERSE SPEAKING

(Preparation for time and rhythm study)
Undivided beat,
33–46–51–57–62
91 (1st)–111–116 (2nd)–123
126 (both)–131 (both)–132–146
Evenly divided beat,
32–33–36(both)–58–140
6/8 rhythm,
68–86–112–152

GENERAL CLASSIFICATIONS

Title	*Page*
Ant Reporter Interviews the Bees, The (A very small opera)	72
Around the Calendar (Songs of the seasons and special days of the school year)	82
At Home	5
Singing with the Grownups	23
Cobbler and the Elves, The	153
Descants	13–41–47–48–88–103 115–136–143–149
For Christmas	176
Fun with Phrases	171
Going Here and There in All Kinds of Weather (Songs of transportation, sunshine, rain, wind, etc.)	59
Going to the Circus	54
Great Big Out-of-Doors, The	31
Indian's Day, An (Songs which may be used in an original song play)	77
Let's Sing These Songs All by Ourselves (Reading songs)	130
Making Believe (Songs of fun and fancy)	140
Music Road, The	119
Songs for Study	119
Songs for Reading	130
Songs for Rhythm Study	136
Singing Games	180
Shopping (Songs of Community Life)	42
Things That Go, Fast or Slow (Rhythm study—evenly divided beat)	136
Tuneful Tim's Letter (Creative suggestions)	117
We Sing, Play and Dance (Action, dance and rhythm band)	106

Reproductions, in color, of 12 famous paintings for study in connection with individual songs or groups of songs, may be obtained from the publishers of this book, or directly from The Art Extension Press, Westport, Connecticut. The pictures are as follows:

Artext print number	*Title of Picture*	*For study with:*
114	Feeding Her Birds	Home; Character (protection)
123	Miss Bowles	Pets; Character (protection, kindliness)
228	Girl with Cat	Pets
107	Boy with Rabbit	Pets; Animals; Character (kindliness)
4	An Aristocrat	Pets; Character (obedience, protection)
16	The Sheepfold	Evening; Animals; Character (care)
162	Saying Grace	Devotion; Thanksgiving
8	Madonna of the Chair	Christmas
161	Indian Harvest	An Indian's Day
206	Men on the Dock	Transportation
119	The Holiday	Nature
95	After a Summer Shower	Wind and Weather; Seasons.

EXAMPLES OF TONAL FIGURES

The figures chosen fall naturally into tone groups for ear training and study and in many cases the entire song is suitable for reading if desired.

So-la-so; so-mi; fa-mi-re-do have been used as the basic figures. These have been chosen because a study of songs of all types has shown them to be the most natural and commonly used. They also lead naturally to simple scale and chordal combinations and to simple cadences.

Sometimes a figure in undivided beat appears in a song which has other rhythmic difficulties. It is listed under undivided beat. Songs in ¢ may be counted in $\frac{4}{4}$ rhythm, if desired, for reading purposes. Figures in this rhythm are listed under undivided beat (quarter note).

Other examples of all of these figures will be found in unlisted songs, but those chosen have seemed the most characteristic groupings for ear training and study.

Figures	*Simple Rhythm Undivided Beat* *Pages*	*More Complicated Rhythm Divided Beat or 6/8*
so-la-so (mi)	17-30-50-72-91-104-110-113-119-123-126-127-128-131	19-21-25-31-37-47-48-60-69-70-73-76-98-109-139-150
so-mi	13-34-40-46-61-62-67-72-88-91-109-115-119-125-126-130-131-138-166	28-32-44-79-82-100-102-108-137-152-158-165
mi-do	13-33-35-37-54-58-63-73-91-92-109-115-117-126-131-138-141-146	37-40-65-71-73-76-84-102-108-152-161-162-165
do-ti-la-so	51-61-62-99-120-122-124-125-126-127-130-132-144-145	15-32-36-102-141
(so) fa-mi-re-do	32-33-48-99-111-119-120-122-126-127-130-131-132-134-135-151	21-33-54-60-70-139-147-150
do-re-mi-fa (so)	17-39-83-88	5-9-14-93-94-100-140-147-169
so-la-ti-do	17-48-83-97-103-104-107-151	5-31-36-94-98-100-142-143
so-mi-do	12-83-110-123-126-127-130-134-141-146	21-28-31-58-98
$\overline{\text{do}}$-so-mi-$\underline{\text{do}}$	120-129-130-132	21-101
mi-so	36-46-61-62-77-96-97-101-109-111-116-126-133-134-136-139-149-151	9-21-35-38-84-116-137
do-mi-so	30-34-106-120-134	21-52-109-150-158
$\underline{\text{do}}$-mi-so-$\overline{\text{do}}$	124-130-134	
re-ti-do	49-96-141	6-7-24-53-55
re-do	31-81-91-96-101-102-111-113-114-125-127-128-132-134-136-138-144-145-169	10-11-85-89-158-161
(so) fa-re-do	36-101-110	18-25-111-143-165
Minor, Pentatonic and Modal Tunes	29-56-57-63-*128-159-160	*19-26-*77-*78-79-*80-*81-90-97

* These pentatonic (5 tone) tunes can be played on the black keys of the piano.

ALPHABETICAL INDEX

Title	*Author*	*Composer or Source*	*Page*
All in the Tree	J. Lilian Vandevere	Ann Weston	39
America	S. F. Smith	Henry Carey	23
An Indian's Day	Trans. from Indian	Indian	77
Ant Reporter Interviews the Bees, The	Margery Armitage	Samuel Lewis	72
Around the Christmas Tree	Mary de Haven	Swedish Carol	178
Baby, Sleep	Trans. P. W. Dykema	French	128
Band Music	Helen Fitch	Jane Landon	132
Big, Big Sky, The	Margery Armitage	Barbara Wentworth	121
Big Brown Bear	Alys Bentley	Alys Bentley	57
Billy Magee Magaw	Traditional	Louis Lambert	26
Break the Piñata	Jane Landon	Mexican Folk Tune	179
Bugle, Blow	Helen Fitch	Ann Weston	134
Busy Clock, A	Harvey W. Loomis	Adolf Jensen	136
Buttercups, Too	David Stevens	Hungarian	101
Butterflies	Helen Call	Mary Root Kern	33
Cat in the Cherry Tree, The	David Stevens	Hungarian	149
Chinese New Year	Sidney Rowe	Far Eastern (Adapted)	128
Christmas Holly	Florence R. Kirk	John V. Pearsall	89
Christmas Snow	Helen Fitch	French Folk Tune	177
Circus Parade	David Stevens	Italian	54
Clown, The	Stephen Fay	David Stevens	55
Cobbler, The	J. Lilian Vandevere	J. Lilian Vandevere	46
Cobbler and the Elves, The	Berta Elsmith	Folk	153
Come, Little Chipmunk	David Stevens	Danish	32
Come, My Ponies	Berta Elsmith	Flemish	165
Cookies	Laura Gibb	Robert W. Gibb	12
Copying Mother	Floy A. Rossman	Floy A. Rossman	9
Cradle Song	Trans. David Stevens	Swedish	29
Daily Express, The	From "Jolly Jingles"	Charles Harvey	68
Dippers and Bears	Ruth Harrison	Slovenian	139
Donkey Music	Harvey W. Loomis	French	147
Down and Back	Jane Landon	Gladys Pitcher	91
Duet, A	M. Theresa Armitage	M. Theresa Armitage	113
Easter Time	Elsie Heath	Elsie Heath	99
Evening Prayer	Berta Elsmith	Finnish	159
Fireman, The	Lowell Bond	Harvey W. Loomis	49
Follow My Leader	Trans. Alice Fletcher	Indian Game Song	79
Foreign Language, A	Felix Goddard	Carl Reinecke	102
Funny Bunny	Cordelia Brooks Fenno	Ukrainian	37
Gay Little Dance, A	Traditional (Adapted)	English Game Song	108
Geese	Floy A. Rossman	Floy A. Rossman	36
Giant Comes, The	Trans. from Flemish	Flemish	150
Going to Boston	Traditional	American Singing Game	185
Good Cows	Helen Fitch	Italian Folk Tune	174
Good Morning	Fannie A. Buchanan	Gladys Pitcher	6
Good Morning, We Say	M. Theresa Armitage	Old Tune (Adapted)	127
Gray Squirrel	Lowell Bond	Czech	84
Grocer Man, The	Floy A. Rossman	Floy A. Rossman	52
Growing	Helen Fitch	Betsy Adams	96
Guess Who I Am	Frederic Manley	Harvey W. Loomis	30
Have You Seen the Zoo?	David Stevens	French	56
He Whistled Just the Same	David Stevens	David Stevens	21
Hello!	Harvey W. Loomis	Harvey W. Loomis	35
High, Low	M. Theresa Armitage	M. Theresa Armitage	130
Hippity Hop	Margery Armitage	Harvey W. Loomis	112
Hobby Horse	David Stevens	Japanese	19

Title	*Author*	*Composer or Source*	*Page*
Hop, Little Frog	Floy A. Rossman	Floy A. Rossman	40
Hot Gingerbread	J. Lilian Vandevere	J. Lilian Vandevere	13
How They Grow	Stephen Fay	German	134
Hurdy-Gurdy Man, The	Arthur Henry	Sidney Mason	100
Hy-Ya-Ho	Trans. Ruth Harrison	Indian Dance Song	78
I Walk and Talk with Father	David Stevens	Danish	10
I Want a Pair of Shoes	Berta Elsmith	German	162
I Want to Sail	David Stevens	English Country Dance	141
I'm Learning to Dance	M. Theresa Armitage	Alsatian	107
In a Hickory Nut	James Whitcomb Riley	Victor Pierpont	86
In Fourteen Hundred Ninety-Two	Stephen Fay	David Stevens	83
Jack O' Lantern	Angela Wiechard	Angela Wiechard	85
James, the Brave	J. Lilian Vandevere	Norwegian	144
Jingle Bells	Traditional	Old Song	111
John, the Miller	Traditional	Mexican Singing Game	182
Jolly Miller, The	Stephen Fay	Franz Schubert	53
Jolly Tar, A	Stephen Fay	Harvey W. Loomis	71
Jump Jim Crow	Traditional	American Singing Game	181
June	Harvey W. Loomis	Harvey W. Loomis	102
Lambkin, The	Frederic Manley	Lowell Bond	38
Lightning Bug	M. Theresa Armitage	M. Theresa Armitage	131
Liner and the Tug, The	J. Lilian Vandevere	J. Lilian Vandevere	70
Little Black Cat	David Stevens	German	126
Little Brown Bug	M. Theresa Armitage	Werner Janssen	33
Little Bunny Hops	Floy A. Rossman	Floy A. Rossman	31
Little Turtle, The	Vachel Lindsay	Gladys Pitcher	140
Little Wind	Floy A. Rossman	Floy A. Rossman	61
Long Trip, A	J. Lilian Vandevere	Gladys Pitcher	133
Lullaby	Frances Densmore	Chippewa Indian	81
Making Christmas Presents	Helen Fitch	Jane Landon	176
March Wind	Harvey W. Loomis	Harvey W. Loomis	97
Mary's Lamb	David Stevens	Gladys Pitcher	151
Mince Pie	Stephen Fay	Harvey W. Loomis	87
Minuet		Wolfgang Mozart	95
Miss Chickadee	Frederic Manley	A. Bode	96
Moment Musicale		Franz Schubert	160
Moon-Cake, The	Harvey W. Loomis	Hanoverian (Abridged)	143
Mother's Day	Stephen Fay	Frederick von Flotow	101
Moving Day	Harvey W. Loomis	Harvey W. Loomis	37
Music on the Air	J. Lilian Vandevere	Russian	22
Musical Mix-Up, A	J. Lilian Vandevere	Gladys Pitcher	120
My Christmas Stocking	Verse for Original Tune		178
My Daddy's Watch	Floy A. Rossman	Floy A. Rossman	137
My Fiddle	Hylas Irish	Alys Bentley	116
My Funny Jumping Jack	Harvey W. Loomis	Harvey W. Loomis	18
My Humming Top	Harvey W. Loomis	Harvey W. Loomis	11
My Morning Song	M. Theresa Armitage	M. Theresa Armitage	5
My Present	Pringle Barre	Anna von Wohlfarth-Grille	50
My Shopping List	David Stevens	Westphalian	51
Nelly Bly	Stephen Foster	Stephen Foster	24
New Shoes	J. Lilian Vandevere	Mary de Haven	62
New Simple Simon	David Stevens	Gladys Pitcher	135
Night Winds	Helen Call	Mary Root Kern	134
Noisy Bird, A	Anonymous	Harvey W. Loomis	36
O Look! O Look!	Berta Elsmith	German	161
Occupations	Margery Armitage	Polish	15
Once upon a Time	Berta Elsmith	Bohemian	169
On the Village Green	Ann Weston	Ukrainian	115

Title	*Author*	*Composer or Source*	*Page*
Orange Moon	Harvey W. Loomis (Adapted)	Harvey W. Loomis	41
Our Christmas Pie	Traditional (Adapted)	Old English	90
Our School Bus	David Stevens	Bohemian	67
Penny, Penny	Traditional	Singing Game	184
Pinto and I	Verse for Original Tune		181
Policeman, The	Floy A. Rossman	Floy A. Rossman	44
Ragtag and Bobtail	Harvey W. Loomis	Harvey W. Loomis	16
Rain or Shine	Mercedes Beckman	Anna von Wohlfarth-Grille	60
Rainbow	Margery Armitage	Gladys Pitcher	125
Saint Patrick's Day	Stephen Fay	Irish	98
See That Elephant	Harvey W. Loomis	Harvey W. Loomis	58
Seesaw	Stephen Fay	Barbara Wentworth	130
Shoes	J. Lilian Vandevere	Old Tune	47
Shopping (verse)	David Stevens		42
Short Songs from "Sing with Me"	Jane Landon	French Folk Tune	172
Silent Night	Joseph Mohr	Franz Gruber	25
Sing a Song of Seasons	Robert Louis Stevenson	Harvey W. Loomis	82
Sing with Me	Jane Landon	French Folk Tune	171
Sleepy Song	Maurice Talbot	Old Tune (Adapted)	129
Slumber Song	M. Theresa Armitage	Old Tune	131
Smoking the Peace Pipe	Frances Densmore	Chippewa Indian	80
Song of the Corn	Trans. Alice Fletcher	Indian	79
So-Sow-Sewing	Traditional (Adapted by R. H.)	Old Tune (Adapted)	109
Spanish Dance	Ruth Harrison	Ann Weston	110
Spring Greeting	Trans. David Stevens	Felix Mendelssohn	100
Star	Margery Armitage	Sam Lewis	123
Stately Dance, A	Ruth Harrison	Edvard Grieg	106
Storm Clouds	Margery Armitage	Barbara Wentworth	124
Strange!	Harvey W. Loomis	Harvey W. Loomis	14
Strange Shoes	Jane Landon	French Folk Tune	175
Streamline Trains	Sidney Rowe	German	129
Such a Difference	H. W. Loomis and R. Harrison	Harvey W. Loomis	28
Summer Lullaby	J. Lilian Vandevere	Old Tune	105
Sun and Moon	Margery Armitage	Barbara Wentworth	122
Sunrise Song	Harvey W. Loomis	Zuni Indian	77
Swinging	Floy A. Rossman	Floy A. Rossman	114
Swinging in the Lane	Traditional	American Singing Game	180
Swish!	Floy A. Rossman	Floy A. Rossman	50
Tale of the Tailless Rabbit, The	Harvey W. Loomis	Harvey W. Loomis	142
Tap-a-Tap Tap	Cordelia Brooks Fenno	Bohemian	48
Thanksgiving	Stephen Fay	J. S. Bach	127
Theme		Wolfgang Mozart	147
There once Was a Wren	David Stevens	Old English	152
They're Useful	J. Lilian Vandevere	Gladys Pitcher	62
Three Blind Mice	Margery Armitage	Old Tune	66
Triangle, The	Floy A. Rossman	Floy A. Rossman	111
Trim, Trig Trailer, The	J. Lilian Vandevere	J. Lilian Vandevere	64
Trot, Trot, Trot	Floy A. Rossman	Floy A. Rossman	20
Tune for Original Words		Mary de Haven	177
Tuneful Tim's Letter			117
Twilight	Harvey W. Loomis	French	126
Two Friends	M. Theresa Armitage	M. Theresa Armitage	116
Two Valentines	J. Lilian Vandevere	Mary de Haven	93
Ups and Downs	Ann Flint	Mary Root Kern	130
Wandering	Sidney Rowe	Ann Weston	132
Waves	Stephen Fay	Barbara Wentworth	138
Waves and I, The	Jane Landon	Gladys Pitcher	104
We Give Thanks	Stephen Fay	Gladys Pitcher	88
We Sing as We March	Harvey W. Loomis	Harvey W. Loomis	110

Title	*Author*	*Composer or Source*	*Page*
Weather Vane	Harvey W. Loomis	Harvey W. Loomis	59
What Do They Do?	Trans. by J. L. V.	German Singing Game	183
What I Like	Mercedes Beckman	M. Theresa Armitage	17
When Bands Begin to Play	Stephen Fay	Ann Weston	103
When Good Fortune Comes Tapping	Berta Elsmith	German	166
When Mother Sews	Stephen Fay	Czech	8
When the Postman Comes	David Stevens	Creole	43
Who Has Seen the Wind?	Christina Rossetti	Alys Bentley	63
Why?	Margery Armitage	J. Lilian Vandevere	148
Wind Your Thread	Berta Elsmith	Danish	158
Winter	Harvey W. Loomis	Harvey W. Loomis	91
Winter's Going	Helen Call	Mary Root Kern	97
Wish, A	Hylas Irish	Alys Bentley	34
Wonderful Man of Snow, A	Floy A. Rossman	Floy A. Rossman	92
Woodpecker, The	P. K. Yonge School	P. K. Yonge Laboratory School, Gainesville, Fla., Direction, Miss Cleva J. Carson	11
Yankee Doodle	Traditional	Old Tune	94
Yoo-Hoo	Ruth Harrison	Barbara Wentworth	119
Young Puss	Frederic Manley	Gladys Pitcher	146